Math Engagement
Grade 7

By
M.J. OWEN

COPYRIGHT © 2003 Mark Twain Media, Inc.

ISBN 1-58037-235-X

Printing No. CD-1581

Mark Twain Media, Inc., Publishers
Distributed by Carson-Dellosa Publishing Company, Inc.

Table of Contents

Introduction

Based on the National Council of Teachers of Mathematics (NCTM) Standards, this series provides students with multiple grade-appropriate opportunities to practice each skill. Each book contains several practice pages targeting each skill, as well as an assessment page at the end of each section. The book also includes periodic reviews of multiple skills throughout the book, in addition to a cumulative assessment. Each assessment and review is set up in stan-

NCTM STANDARD

Page no.	Number and Operations	Algebra	Geometry	Measurement	Data Analysis, Probability	Problem Solving	Reasoning, Proof	Communication	Connections	Representation
2	x					x				x
3	x									
4	x									x
5	x									x
6	x									
7	x									
8	x	x								
9	x	x								
10	x	x			x					
11	x									
12	x									
13	x	x								
14	x	x			x					
15	x	x								
16	x	x								x
17	x	x								
18		x								
19		x						x		
20		x			x					x
21		x								x
22		x								x
23		x								
24		x								x
25		x								x
26		x								
27		x								x
28	x	x			x					
29	x	x								
30	x	x								
31	x	x								
32				x						
33	x			x						
34			x	x		x				
35	x			x						
36	x		x	x						
37	x		x	x						
38	x									x
39			x	x						
40		x	x	x						
41		x	x	x						
42		x	x	x						
43		x	x	x						

NCTM STANDARD

Page no.	Number and Operations	Algebra	Geometry	Measurement	Data Analysis, Probability	Problem Solving	Reasoning, Proof	Communication	Connections	Representation
44		x	x	x						
45		x	x	x						
46	x	x	x			x				
47			x				x			
48		x	x							
49	x	x	x							
50	x	x	x				x			
51			x							
52			x							
53			x			x				
54			x							
55			x							
56			x							
57			x						x	
58			x							
59			x							
60			x							
61			x							
62	x		x							
63			x			x				x
64			x							
65			x				x			
66					x		x	x	x	
67					x	x				
68					x		x	x	x	
69					x					x
70					x					
71					x	x		x	x	
72					x					
73					x					
74			x	x						
75	x		x							
76			x							
77					x	x				
78					x					
79					x					
80					x					
81					x					
82					x					
83	x		x							
84	x		x	x	x					
85	x		x	x	x					

Name: _____   Date: _____

Skill: Understanding numbers, ways of representing numbers, relationships among numbers, and number systems

Unit 1: Number and Operations: *Practice Activity 1*

Name the place of the number in bold. ***Example:*** 8,652.03 The bold number is in the tens place.

1. 4,**8**67,291 _____   6. 0.5**9**3 _____

2. **3**1,281,471 _____   7. 8,507,**2**11 _____

3. 1,**6**89,740 _____   8. 25,609.4**5** _____

4. **5**1,087,481 _____   9. 26.1**5**8 _____

5. 1,792.3**1** _____   10. 0.00**4**6 _____

Write each number in word form. ***Example:*** 7,901,052.5 The number written in word form is seven million, nine hundred one thousand, fifty-two and five tenths.

11. 4,786,921 _____

12. 33,781,441 _____

13. 2,468,291 _____

14. 17,264,521 _____

15. 452.097 _____

Write each number in standard form. ***Example:*** The number forty-two million, three hundred ten thousand, four hundred five is written in standard form as 42,310,405.

16. seven hundred million _____

17. sixteen thousand, four hundred eighty-eight _____

18. seventy-five thousand, four _____

19. sixty-five million, fifty-eight _____

20. one hundred seventy-three and thirteen hundredths _____

WAKE-UP WORD PROBLEM: Arlene saved $21 in June, $58 in July, and $63 in August. Peggy saved four times as much as Arlene during the same three-month period. How much money did Peggy save?

_____

Name: _____ Date: _____

Skill: Understanding numbers, ways of representing numbers, relationships among numbers, and number systems

Unit 1: Number and Operations: *Practice Activity 2*

Just a Tip: If you have trouble determining the larger number, try converting each fraction and/or decimal to a percent, ratio, and/or decimal. Then compare the numbers again.

Put the decimals in order from least to greatest.

1. 0.066, 7.62, 0.092, 0.041   _____

2. 7.28, 0.826, 0.043, 0.034   _____

3. 0.27, 2.7, 0.789, 0.045   _____

4. 0.321, 32.1, 3.21, 4.05   _____

5. 0.78, 0.75, 0.65, 0.29   _____

Put the decimals in order from greatest to least.

6. 0.011, 0.012, 1.5, 15.7   _____

7. 0.068, 0.072, 0.077, 0.61   _____

8. 0.65, 0.56, 5.75, 0.290   _____

9. 0.395, 0.405, 30.7, 2.35   _____

10. 4.11, 0.276, 0.288, 0.028   _____

Put the fractions in order from least to greatest.

11. $\frac{1}{3}, \frac{5}{8}, \frac{3}{4}, \frac{1}{2}$ _____

12. $\frac{1}{3}, \frac{1}{4}, \frac{7}{9}, \frac{5}{11}$ _____

Put the fractions in order from greatest to least.

13. $\frac{1}{2}, \frac{3}{4}, \frac{5}{7}, \frac{3}{5}$ _____

14. $\frac{2}{3}, \frac{1}{3}, \frac{5}{9}$ _____

15. $\frac{5}{12}, \frac{7}{8}, \frac{1}{3}, \frac{1}{4}$ _____

3

Name: _____ Date: _____

Skill: Understanding numbers, ways of representing numbers, relationships among numbers, and number systems

Unit 1: Number and Operations: *Practice Activity 3*

In a number such as 5^2, the 5 is the **base** and the ^{2} is the **exponent**. The exponent indicates how many times the base is to be multiplied. For example, in 5^2, the ^{2} tells you to multiply the 5 two times. $5^2 = 5 \times 5 = 25$.

When a base number has an exponent, the base number is said to be raised to the indicated power, so 5^2 is read as "5 to the second power."

Just a Tip: Any base raised to the zero power equals one. $3^0 = 1$, $10^0 = 1$
Any base raised to the first power equals the base. $3^1 = 3$, $10^1 = 10$

Raise the following bases to the indicated powers.

1. 6^2 _____
2. 8^4 _____
3. 2^7 _____
4. 5^1 _____
5. 9^0 _____

6. 10^2 _____
7. 10^3 _____
8. 10^4 _____
9. 10^5 _____
10. 10^6 _____

Scientific notation is a way to write large numbers in a smaller space using exponents to indicate the powers of 10. First move the decimal point just to the right of the number in the farthest left place. Then you multiply that number by 10 raised to the number of decimal places you moved over.

Example: 3,829   Move the decimal point to 3.829.
The number can now be written as 3.829×10^3.
You can check the number by multiplying $3.829 \times (10 \times 10 \times 10) = 3.829 \times 1,000 = 3,829$.
If you have a number like 700, you can drop the zeros when writing scientific notation.
    $700 = 7 \times 10^2$

Rewrite each number in scientific notation.

11. 900 _____
12. 500,000 _____
13. 2,704,000 _____
14. 65.81 _____
15. 400,000,000 _____

16. 78,410,000,000 _____
17. 768.7 _____
18. 80,000,000 _____
19. 3,000 _____
20. 6,842,700,000 _____

Name: _____ Date: _____

Skill: Understanding numbers, ways of representing numbers, relationships among numbers, and number systems

Unit 1: Number and Operations: *Practice Activity 4*

Write each decimal in number form.

1. nine tenths _____

2. seventeen hundredths _____

3. eight tenths _____

4. sixty-three hundredths _____

5. one and four tenths _____

6. seventy-two thousandths _____

Just a Tip: You can divide the numerator by the denominator to find each fraction in decimal form.

Find a decimal equal to each fraction.

7. $\frac{3}{5}$ _____

8. $\frac{7}{8}$ _____

9. $\frac{1}{2}$ _____

10. $\frac{3}{4}$ _____

11. $\frac{6}{9}$ _____

12. $\frac{2}{3}$ _____

13. $\frac{1}{4}$ _____

14. $\frac{5}{6}$ _____

15. $\frac{3}{8}$ _____

Name: _____ Date: _____

Skill: Understanding numbers, ways of representing numbers, relationships among numbers, and number systems

Unit 1: Number and Operations: *Assessment 1*

Mark the answer that names the value of each number in bold.

1. 268,749
   - ○ A. six million
   - ○ B. six hundred thousand
   - ○ C. six thousand
   - ○ D. sixty thousand

2. 13,741,268
   - ○ A. three million
   - ○ B. three hundred thousand
   - ○ C. thirty thousand
   - ○ D. thirty-seven million

Mark the answer that shows each number in word form.

3. 17,642,741
   - ○ A. seven million, six hundred forty-two thousand, seven hundred forty-one
   - ○ B. seventeen million, six hundred thousand, seven hundred and forty-one
   - ○ C. seventeen million, six hundred forty-two thousand, seven hundred forty-one
   - ○ D. seventeen million, six hundred forty-two, seven hundred forty-one

4. 387,291,202
   - ○ A. three hundred eighty-seven billion, two hundred ninety-one thousand, two hundred two
   - ○ B. three hundred eighty-seven million, two hundred ninety-one thousand, two hundred two
   - ○ C. three hundred eighteen million, two hundred ninety-one thousand, two hundred two
   - ○ D. three hundred eighty-seven million, two hundred nineteen thousand, two hundred two

Mark the answer that shows each number in standard form.

5. seventeen million, eight hundred ninety-two
   - ○ A. 17,892
   - ○ B. 17,892,000
   - ○ C. 17,000,892
   - ○ D. 17,000,802

6. four hundred thousand, six hundred one
   - ○ A. 400,610
   - ○ B. 4,000,601
   - ○ C. 400,601
   - ○ D. 4,000,601

Name: _____ Date: _____

Unit 1: Number and Operations: *Assessment 1 (cont.)*

Mark the answer that puts the decimals in order from least to greatest.

7. 0.051, 0.51, 0.63, 0.74
- ○ A. 0.51, 0.63, 0.74, 0.051
- ○ B. 0.051, 0.51, 0.63, 0.74
- ○ C. 0.051, 0.51, 0.74, 0.63
- ○ D. 0.74, 0.63, 0.51, 0.051

Mark the answer that puts the decimals in order from greatest to least.

8. 0.29, 0.41, 0.44, 0.027
- ○ A. 0.44, 0.41, 0.027, 0.29
- ○ B. 0.027, 0.29, 0.41, 0.44
- ○ C. 0.027, 0.44, 0.41, 0.027
- ○ D. 0.44, 0.41, 0.29, 0.027

Mark the answer that puts the fractions in order from least to greatest.

9. $\frac{2}{5}, \frac{1}{3}, \frac{5}{11}, \frac{6}{7}$
- ○ A. $\frac{5}{11}, \frac{1}{3}, \frac{2}{5}, \frac{6}{7}$
- ○ B. $\frac{1}{3}, \frac{2}{5}, \frac{5}{11}, \frac{6}{7}$
- ○ C. $\frac{2}{5}, \frac{5}{11}, \frac{1}{3}, \frac{6}{7}$
- ○ D. $\frac{6}{7}, \frac{1}{3}, \frac{5}{11}, \frac{2}{5}$

Mark the answer that puts the fractions in order from greatest to least.

10. $\frac{11}{12}, \frac{1}{2}, \frac{3}{5}, \frac{7}{9}$
- ○ A. $\frac{1}{2}, \frac{11}{12}, \frac{7}{9}, \frac{3}{5}$
- ○ B. $\frac{11}{12}, \frac{7}{9}, \frac{3}{5}, \frac{1}{2}$
- ○ C. $\frac{11}{12}, \frac{3}{5}, \frac{7}{9}, \frac{1}{2}$
- ○ D. $\frac{7}{9}, \frac{3}{5}, \frac{1}{2}, \frac{11}{12}$

Mark the answer that shows each decimal in number form.

11. seven and eight tenths
- ○ A. 7.08
- ○ B. 7.80
- ○ C. 78.0
- ○ D. 7.18

12. forty-eight hundredths
- ○ A. 0.48
- ○ B. 0.048
- ○ C. 4.8
- ○ D. 48.0

Mark the decimal that is equivalent to each fraction.

13. $\frac{5}{11}$
- ○ A. 0.045
- ○ B. 0.21
- ○ C. 0.50
- ○ D. 0.45

14. $\frac{3}{4}$
- ○ A. 7.50
- ○ B. 0.725
- ○ C. 0.025
- ○ D. 0.75

Mark the answer that expresses the following number in scientific notation.

15. 9,025,000,000
- ○ A. $9,025 \times 10^5$
- ○ B. 9.025×10^6
- ○ C. 9.025×10^9
- ○ D. 9.025×10^{10}

Name: _____   Date: _____

Skill: Understanding the meanings of operations and how they relate to one another

Unit 1: Number and Operations: *Practice Activity 5*

Just a Tip: It is important to know the order in which you should perform arithmetic operations. First, do any operations in parentheses and perform any exponentiation. Next, perform multiplication and division from left to right. Finally, perform addition and subtraction from left to right.

Solve each problem. Do not use a calculator.

1. $8 \times 16 \div 2 =$ _____

2. $25 \times 4 \div 10 =$ _____

3. $27 - 4 \times 6 =$ _____

4. $38 - 5 \times 12 =$ _____

5. $48 \div 2 + 24 \div 6 =$ _____

6. $9 \times 9 \div 9 =$ _____

7. $17 + 7 \times 6 =$ _____

8. $90 - 2^2 \times 4 =$ _____

9. $56 \div 2 + 88 =$ _____

10. $78 - 14 - 25 =$ _____

11. $35 + 4^4 =$ _____

12. $30 - 2^2 \times 5 =$ _____

13. $7(36 \div 4) \div (8 - 5) =$ _____

14. $(12 - 7)^2 \times (4 + 5) =$ _____

15. $(32 + 4) \div (21 - 18)^2 =$ _____

Extension Activity: Have students write three problems and exchange with their classmates to solve each set of problems.

Name: _____ Date: _____

Skill: Understanding the meanings of operations and how they relate to one another

Unit 1: Number and Operations: *Practice Activity 6*

Just a Tip: Remember to substitute the correct value for each variable.

Perform exponentiation first. If a constant and a variable are written together, perform the multiplication or division indicated in that grouping first before continuing with other multiplication or division.

> **Example:**   If $b = 4$ and $d = 3$, $12/b \times 2d =$
> $3 \times 6 = 18$ NOT $12 \div 4 \times 2 \times 3 = 18$

Evaluate each algebraic expression if $b = 4$, $c = 7$, and $d = 3$.

1. $3b + c^2 - 4 =$ _____

2. $bc^4 =$ _____

3. $9c - 2b =$ _____

4. $24 \times b \div 2d =$ _____

5. $c + c + c - d =$ _____

6. $7c + b^2 =$ _____

7. $8d^3 =$ _____

8. $12b + 2d \div 6 =$ _____

9. $6b - 2d =$ _____

10. $b/2 - 18 \times 4 =$ _____

11. $bc^2 =$ _____

12. $5c \times 4b - 2d =$ _____

13. $9d + 2bd^2 =$ _____

14. $(c - d) \times b^3 =$ _____

15. $(c^2 + 5) \div d =$ _____

Name: _____   Date: _____

Skill: Understanding the meanings of operations and how they relate to one another

Unit 1: Number and Operations: *Practice Activity 7*

Use the order of operations to evaluate each expression.

Just a Tip: Work inside the parentheses before doing anything else.

1. 18 + 4(22 - 8) = _____

2. (45 - 4) x 6 = _____

3. $(8^2 + 12)$ - 24 = _____

4. 8(12 - 8) + 42 + 8(10 - 2) = _____

5. 6(18 - 6) + 35 + 5(18 - 6) = _____

6. 32 + 6(14 - 7) = _____

7. $(6^3 + 4(12 - 2))$ - (34 - 6) = _____

8. $(4^5 + 8(18 - 4))$ - (28 - 6) = _____

9. 5(14 x 9) - 8 = _____

10. 8(12 x 12) - 15 = _____

11. 8(6 - 4) + 28 = _____

12. 12(15 - 5) + 38 = _____

WAKE-UP WORD PROBLEM: Charlene saves the money she usually spends on snacks for six weeks. The first week she saves $0.85. The second week she saves twice as much money as the first week, the third week she saves three times as much money as the first week, the fourth week she saves four times as much, the fifth week she saves five times as much, and the sixth week she saves six times as much. How much money does Charlene save during the entire six weeks?

_____

Name: _____ Date: _____

Skill: Understanding the meanings of operations and how they relate to one another

Unit 1: Number and Operations: *Practice Activity 8*

The **radical** sign $\sqrt{}$ over a number called the **radicand** means you are to find the square root of the radicand. The **square root** is the number that, when squared (multiplied by itself), equals the radicand. Each number has two square roots, a positive number and a negative number.

Example: $\sqrt{81}$ = 9 or -9 or ±9   9 x 9 = 81   -9 x -9 = 81

Find the square roots of each number without using a calculator.

1. $\sqrt{25}$ _____

2. $\sqrt{16}$ _____

3. $\sqrt{4}$ _____

4. $\sqrt{36}$ _____

5. $\sqrt{100}$ _____

6. $\sqrt{121}$ _____

7. $\sqrt{9}$ _____

8. $\sqrt{81}$ _____

9. $\sqrt{49}$ _____

10. $\sqrt{64}$ _____

Give the square roots of each number. You may use a calculator. Round the roots to the thousandths place.

11. $\sqrt{12}$ _____

12. $\sqrt{24}$ _____

13. $\sqrt{18}$ _____

14. $\sqrt{0.5}$ _____

15. $\sqrt{2}$ _____

11

Name: _____ Date: _____

Skill: Understanding the meanings of operations and how they relate to one another

Unit 1: Number and Operations: *Assessment 2*

Evaluate each expression. Do not use a calculator. Mark the correct answer.

1. $186 \div 14 \times 6 =$
   - ○ A. 79.71
   - ○ B. 7.791
   - ○ C. 79.851
   - ○ D. 78.87

2. $98 - 2^6 \times 14 =$
   - ○ A. 798
   - ○ B. -798
   - ○ C. 476
   - ○ D. -70

Evaluate each expression if $a = 12$, $b = 16$, and $c = 8$. Mark the correct answer.

3. $4a \div 6 \times 9 =$
   - ○ A. -72
   - ○ B. 68
   - ○ C. 72
   - ○ D. 70

4. $4ab^2 \div 0.02 =$
   - ○ A. 6.140
   - ○ B. 61.440
   - ○ C. 61,440
   - ○ D. 614,400

5. $42 + b/c - \frac{1}{2} =$
   - ○ A. 48
   - ○ B. $43\frac{3}{4}$
   - ○ C. $44\frac{1}{4}$
   - ○ D. $43\frac{1}{2}$

Use the order of operations to evaluate each expression. Mark the correct answer.

6. $45(12 \times 12) - 4^3$
   - ○ A. 6.446
   - ○ B. 6,418
   - ○ C. 6,416
   - ○ D. 6,787

7. $(12^2 + 18) \times 15 =$
   - ○ A. 2,430
   - ○ B. 2,441
   - ○ C. 2,034
   - ○ D. 2,450

8. $42(18 - 6) + 181 =$
   - ○ A. 685
   - ○ B. 586
   - ○ C. 605
   - ○ D. 698

Find the square root of the number. Mark the correct answer.

9. $\sqrt{188}$
   - ○ A. ±13.51
   - ○ B. ±13.71
   - ○ C. ±13.81
   - ○ D. ±5.261

10. $\sqrt{18}$
   - ○ A. ±4.76
   - ○ B. ±4.004
   - ○ C. ±4.24
   - ○ D. ±424

Name: _____ Date: _____

Skill: Computing fluently and making reasonable estimates

Unit 1: Number and Operations: *Practice Activity 9*

Solve each problem.

1. 0.295 + 0.148 = _____

2. 0.076 - 0.021 = _____

3. 4.12 + 8.07 = _____

4. 6.08 - 0.74 = _____

5. 0.396 - 0.271 = _____

6. 5.897 - 4.128 = _____

7. $\frac{3}{4} + \frac{1}{8}$ = _____

8. $\frac{7}{9} + \frac{1}{6}$ = _____

9. $\frac{3}{4} + \frac{7}{8}$ = _____

10. $2\frac{1}{4} - 1\frac{1}{2}$ = _____

11. $3\frac{1}{3} - 1\frac{1}{9}$ = _____

12. $5\frac{1}{2} + 1\frac{1}{4}$ = _____

Just a Tip: An algorithm is a sequence of steps that leads to a desired result. Some algorithms, like long division, can involve many steps.

Analyze each algorithm.

13. 2,978 ÷ 18 = _____

14. 7,429 ÷ 21 = _____

15. 52.86 ÷ 14 = _____

16. 2,179 ÷ 5 = _____

17. 43.20 ÷ 12 = _____

18. 8,261 ÷ 17 = _____

19. 7,389 ÷ 15 = _____

20. 2,158 ÷ 19 = _____

21. 32,746 ÷ 24 = _____

22. 4,769 ÷ 13 = _____

23. 57.80 ÷ 6 = _____

24. 1,442 ÷ 6 = _____

25. 36,215 ÷ 4 = _____

Name: _____   Date: _____

Skill: Computing fluently and making reasonable estimates

Unit 1: Number and Operations: *Practice Activity 10*

Analyze each algorithm.

1. 0.489 - 0.006 = _____

2. 0.297 + 0.328 = _____

3. 4,265 ÷ 27 = _____

4. 3,781 ÷ 19 = _____

5. $2\frac{1}{8}$ x $1\frac{1}{4}$ = _____

6. $6\frac{1}{3}$ x $5\frac{1}{2}$ = _____

7. 0.465 x 0.212 = _____

8. 7.02 x 0.61 = _____

9. $1\frac{1}{2}$ x $1\frac{1}{2}$ = _____

10. 1,275 ÷ 4 = _____

WAKE-UP WORD PROBLEM: Theresa wants to divide 1,568 marbles into 18 piles. How many marbles will Theresa put in each pile? How many, if any, marbles will be left over?

_____

Just a Tip: A proportion is a statement that two fractions are equal. To solve a proportion, find the number that keeps the statement equal.

> ***Example:*** $\frac{4}{8} = \frac{x}{2}$ To find *x*, cross multiply 4 x 2, and then divide by 8.
> $x = 1$

Solve each proportion. Show your work.

11. $\frac{56}{4} = \frac{x}{2}$ _____

12. $\frac{12}{b} = \frac{24}{6}$ _____

13. $\frac{68}{2} = \frac{x}{4}$ _____

14. $\frac{18}{9} = \frac{y}{45}$ _____

15. $\frac{90}{10} = \frac{y}{8}$ _____

16. $\frac{21}{3} = \frac{x}{6}$ _____

17. $\frac{12}{36} = \frac{y}{27}$ _____

18. $\frac{8}{5} = \frac{y}{3}$ _____

19. $\frac{36}{6} = \frac{x}{12}$ _____

20. $\frac{58}{2} = \frac{112}{y}$ _____

Name: _____ Date: _____

Skill: Computing fluently and making reasonable estimates

Unit 1: Number and Operations: *Assessment 3*

Solve each problem and mark the correct answer.

1. $0.567 - 0.001 =$
   - ○ A. 0.506
   - ○ B. 0.566
   - ○ C. 5.66
   - ○ D. 5.76

2. $3\frac{1}{4} - 1\frac{1}{2} =$
   - ○ A. $17\frac{1}{2}$
   - ○ B. $7\frac{3}{4}$
   - ○ C. $1\frac{7}{8}$
   - ○ D. $1\frac{3}{4}$

3. $4,456 \div 4.6 =$
   - ○ A. 9.070
   - ○ B. 9.70
   - ○ C. 96.70
   - ○ D. 968.70

4. $56.70 \div 2.4 =$
   - ○ A. 2.63
   - ○ B. 23.63
   - ○ C. 2.0673
   - ○ D. 236.3

5. $1\frac{7}{8} \times 2\frac{1}{4} =$
   - ○ A. 4
   - ○ B. $4\frac{7}{32}$
   - ○ C. $4\frac{1}{4}$
   - ○ D. $4\frac{7}{8}$

6. $0.0658 - 0.0033 =$
   - ○ A. 6.25
   - ○ B. 0.0625
   - ○ C. 0.7265
   - ○ D. 62.5

7. $5\frac{1}{4} \times 3\frac{1}{8} =$
   - ○ A. $16\frac{13}{32}$
   - ○ B. $16\frac{1}{2}$
   - ○ C. $16\frac{5}{6}$
   - ○ D. $16\frac{3}{32}$

8. $6,789 \div 12 =$
   - ○ A. 567.05
   - ○ B. 565.75
   - ○ C. 578.09
   - ○ D. 5654.32

Solve each problem and mark the correct answer. Show your work.

9. $\frac{110}{10} = \frac{y}{5}$
   - ○ A. $y = 75$
   - ○ B. $y = 45$
   - ○ C. $y = 55$
   - ○ D. $y = 32$

10. $\frac{65}{x} = \frac{72}{4}$
   - ○ A. $x = 3.79$
   - ○ B. $x = 4.02$
   - ○ C. $x = 3.795$
   - ○ D. $x = 3.611$

Name: _____ Date: _____

Review of Three Previously Taught NCTM Standards

- **Understanding numbers, ways of representing numbers, relationships among numbers, and number systems**

- **Understanding the meanings of operations and how they relate to one another**

- **Computing fluently and making reasonable estimates**

1. Mark the correct answer that names the place of the number in bold: 67,9**8**7,908
   - ○ A. hundred thousands
   - ○ B. millions
   - ○ C. ten millions
   - ○ D. billions

2. Which answer represents the number in standard form?
   Sixteen million, four hundred eighty-six thousand, two hundred twelve
   - ○ A. 16,486,221
   - ○ B. 164,862
   - ○ C. 16,586,241
   - ○ D. 16,486,212

3. Mark the answer that puts the fractions in order from least to greatest. $\frac{1}{6}, \frac{7}{8}, \frac{1}{4}, \frac{1}{2}$
   - ○ A. $\frac{1}{6}, \frac{1}{4}, \frac{7}{8}, \frac{1}{2}$
   - ○ B. $\frac{7}{8}, \frac{1}{2}, \frac{1}{4}, \frac{1}{6}$
   - ○ C. $\frac{1}{4}, \frac{1}{6}, \frac{1}{2}, \frac{7}{8}$
   - ○ D. $\frac{1}{6}, \frac{1}{4}, \frac{1}{2}, \frac{7}{8}$

4. Which answer shows the number 50.8 in scientific notation?
   - ○ A. 5.08×10^1
   - ○ B. 5.08×10^2
   - ○ C. 50.8×10^3
   - ○ D. 50.8×10^4

Evaluate each algebraic expression if $a = 2$, $b = 3.5$, and $c = 4$. Mark the correct answer.

5. $5c + b - 8 =$
   - ○ A. 9.150
   - ○ B. 15.9
   - ○ C. 15.5
   - ○ D. 1.50

6. $a/c - \frac{1}{8} \times 15b =$
   - ○ A. -6.0625
   - ○ B. 6.0625
   - ○ C. -3.456
   - ○ D. 3.456

Name: _____ Date: _____

Review of Three Previously Taught NCTM Standards (cont.)

Use the order of operations to evaluate each expression. Mark the correct answer.

7. (89 - 5) x 21 =
- ○ A. 1,768
- ○ B. 1,764
- ○ C. 1,647
- ○ D. 1,567

8. $(9^5 + 8(12 - 5)) - (90 - 65) =$
- ○ A. 58,070
- ○ B. 59,080
- ○ C. 61,061
- ○ D. 58,789

9. $\dfrac{155}{y} = \dfrac{210}{5}$
- ○ A. $y = 3.75$
- ○ B. $y = 3.69$
- ○ C. $y = 3.41$
- ○ D. $y = 3.95$

10. $\dfrac{3}{78} = \dfrac{9}{a}$
- ○ A. $a = 26$
- ○ B. $a = 118$
- ○ C. $a = 234$
- ○ D. $a = 245$

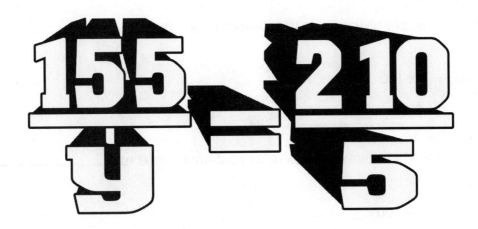

Name: _____ Date: _____

Skill: Understanding patterns, relations, and functions

Unit 2: Algebra: *Practice Activity 1*

Just a Tip: A **variable** is a symbol that can stand for any one of a set of numbers.

Substitute a variable or variables to describe each pattern. First, look at the example.

Example: $4 \times 1 = 4$ $7 \times 1 = 7$ $9 \times 1 = 9$

Substitute a variable: $n \times 1 = n$

Example: $5 + 10 = 10 + 5$ $8 + 12 = 12 + 8$ $7 + 5 = 5 + 7$

Substitute a variable or variables: $x + y = y + x$

1. $4 \times 3 = 3 \times 4$

   $6 \times 5 = 5 \times 6$

   $7.5 \times 2 = 2 \times 7.5$

   Substitute a variable or variables to represent each pattern: _____

2. $\frac{2}{3} \times \frac{2}{3} \times \frac{2}{3} = \left(\frac{2}{3}\right)^3$

   $5 \times 5 \times 5 = 5^3$

   $0.7 \times 0.7 \times 0.7 = 0.7^3$

   Substitute a variable or variables to represent each pattern: _____

3. $75\% \text{ of } 100 = \frac{3}{4} \times 100$

   $75\% \text{ of } \frac{3}{9} = \frac{3}{4} \times \frac{3}{9}$

   $75\% \text{ of } {-55} = \frac{3}{4} \times {-55}$

   Substitute a variable or variables to represent each pattern: _____

4. $25\% \text{ of } 100 = \frac{1}{4} \text{ of } 100$

   $25\% \text{ of } \frac{7}{8} = \frac{1}{4} \text{ of } \frac{7}{8}$

   $25\% \text{ of } {-80} = \frac{1}{4} \text{ of } {-80}$

   Substitute a variable or variables to represent each pattern: _____

Name: _____ Date: _____

Skill: Understanding patterns, relations, and functions

Unit 2: Algebra: *Practice Activity 2*

Describe each pattern using variables.

Example: One person has two legs. Two people have four legs.
Three people have six legs. Four people have eight legs.

Think: 1 person = 1 x 2 legs   2 people = 2 x 2 legs
        3 people = 3 x 2 legs   4 people = 4 x 2 legs
Then, write the things that are the same in each description:
_____ people have 2 legs each.
So, the pattern using variables should be written as:
p people have *p* x 2 legs in all.

1. One insect has six legs. Two insects have twelve legs.
    Three insects have eighteen legs. Four insects have twenty-four legs.

    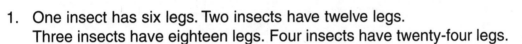

    Now, write the things that are the same in each description:

    _____

    So, the pattern using variables should be written as:

    _____

2. One octopus has eight arms. Two octopuses have sixteen arms.
    Three octopuses have twenty-four arms. Four octopuses have thirty-two arms.

    Now, write the things that are the same in each description:

    _____

    So, the pattern using variables should be written as:

    _____

3. One dime has a value of $0.10. Five dimes have a value of $0.50.
    Eight dimes have a value of $0.80. Ten dimes have a value of $1.00.

    Now, write the things that are the same in each description:

    _____

    So, the pattern using variables should be written as:

    _____

Extension Activity: Have students create some of their own real-life situations, like the ones above, and substitute variables.

Name: _____ Date: _____

Skill: Understanding patterns, relations, and functions

Unit 2: Algebra: *Practice Activity 3*

1. Kelly graphs the amount of money she earns each weekend running her lemonade stand. The first weekend she earns $18. The second weekend she earns $21. The third weekend she earns $24. The fourth weekend she earns $27, and the fifth weekend she earns $30. Let *e* be the amount of money that Kelly earned and *w* be the weekends that she earned the money. On the line, write an equation relating *e* and *w*. Then graph your equation on the graph.

_____

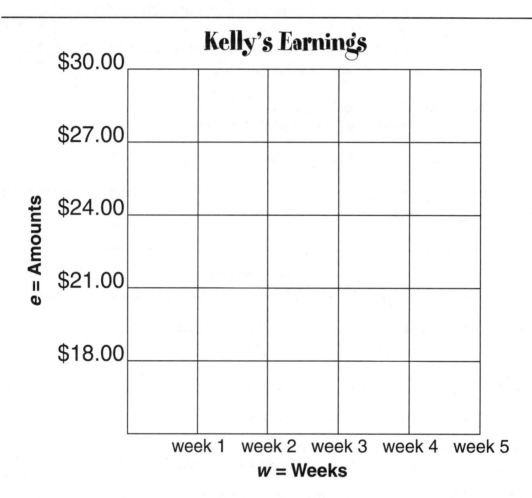

WAKE-UP WORD PROBLEM: Louise has $197.55 in the bank at the beginning of the summer. She doubles the amount of money she has in her account during the first month of summer. Then, she spends just one-third of the amount of money in her account when she vacations at the beach with her best friend. How much money does Louise have in her account now?

Name: _____ Date: _____

Skill: Understanding patterns, relations, and functions

Unit 2: Algebra: *Practice Activity 4*

Find two points that would work in the given equation. Graph the line for the two points, and then check with a third point.

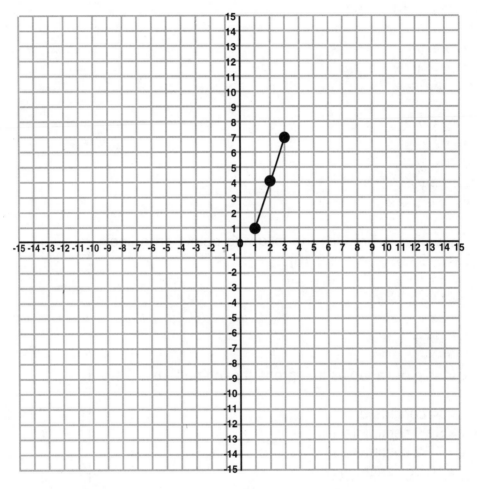

The first one is completed as an example.

1. $y = 3x - 2$
   (1,1) with $x = 1$, $y = 1$
   (2,4) with $x = 2$, $y = 4$
   check point (3,7) with $x = 3$, $y = 7$

2. $y = -1x + 2$
   _____
   _____
   check point _____

3. $y = 2x - 3$
   _____
   _____
   check point _____

4. $y = 2x - 5$
   _____
   _____
   check point _____

Name: _____ Date: _____

Skill: Understanding patterns, relations, and functions

Unit 2: Algebra: *Assessment 1*

Substitute a variable or variables to represent each pattern.

1. $5.60 + 7.10 = 7.10 + 5.60$
   - ○ A. $x + y = y + x$
   - ○ B. $y - x = y - x$
   - ○ C. $x \cdot y = y \cdot x$
   - ○ D. $3x \cdot 2y$

2. $7 \times 12 = 12 \times 7$
   - ○ A. $abc = cba$
   - ○ B. $x - y = y - x$
   - ○ C. $x \cdot y = y \cdot x$
   - ○ D. $x + y = y + x$

3. Find an equation to produce the following points on a line:
   (1,0), (2,-4), (3,-8), (4,-12), (5,-16)
   - ○ A. $y = 5x - 3$
   - ○ B. $y = 1x - 3$
   - ○ C. $y = 2x + 2$
   - ○ D. $y = -4x + 4$

Substitute a variable or variables to represent each pattern.

4. 1 inch = 2.54 centimeters
   2 inches = 5.08 centimeters
   3 inches = 7.62 centimeters
   4 inches = 10.16 centimeters
   - ○ A. $y \cdot 2.54$
   - ○ B. $y \cdot x$
   - ○ C. y (# of inches) = $5.14x$ (# of inches)
   - ○ D. y (# of centimeters) = $2.54x$ (# of inches)

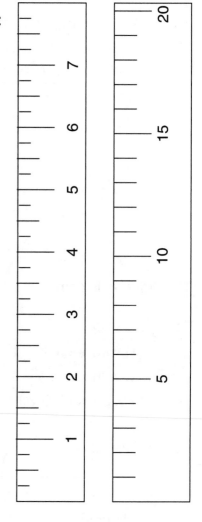

Name: _____ Date: _____

Unit 2: Algebra: *Assessment 1 (cont.)*

Find the pattern and reduce to a formula using variables.

5. Measure the interior angles of a polygon.
   (a) a three-sided figure is one triangle, which is to be known as 180 degrees
   (b) a four-sided figure contains two triangles; at 180 degrees each, that is 2(180) = 360 degrees
   (c) a five-sided figure contains three triangles; at 180 degrees each, that's 3(180) = 540 degrees
   (d) an eight-sided figure contains six triangles; at 180 degrees each, that's 6(180) = 1,080 degrees
   ○ A. *M* (measure of interior angle) x 180
   ○ B. *M* (measure of interior angle) = *N* (number of sides of polygon)
   ○ C. *M* (measure of interior angle) = (*N* (number of sides of polygon) - 2) x 180
   ○ D. 180 x 4

6. Which of the following graphs is the graph of equation $y = 4x \cdot 3$?

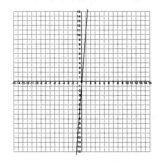 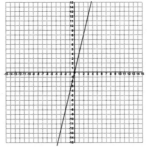 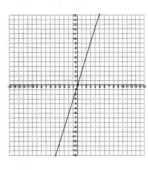 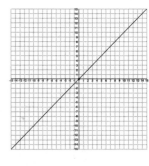

   ○ A.   ○ B.   ○ C.   ○ D.

7. Which of the following graphs is the graph of equation $y = 3x - 1$?

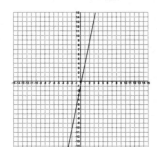 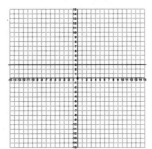 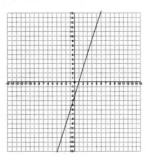 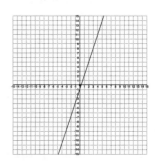

   ○ A.   ○ B.   ○ C.   ○ D.

Name: _____ Date: _____

Skill: Representing and analyzing mathematical situations and structures using algebraic symbols

Unit 2: Algebra: *Practice Activity 5*

Just a Tip: An algebraic expression contains a variable alone or a variable with number and operation symbols.

Examples: Five less than eight: 8 - 5
Four decreased by three times a number: 4 - 3*b*

Write out each expression below in numbers and symbols.

1. ten less four _____

2. the product of six and seven _____

3. five more than one-half a number _____

4. six more than a number, divided by two _____

5. the square of a number, decreased by five _____

6. nineteen less seven _____

7. the product of seven and two _____

8. seven less than four _____

9. the square of a number, decreased by eight _____

10. five more than eight times a number _____

11. six times a number added to the product of four and three _____

12. the quotient of sixty-four divided by four _____

13. ten more than a number multiplied by eight _____

14. a number divided by seven _____

15. eleven decreased by four times a number _____

Name: _____ Date: _____

Skill: Representing and analyzing mathematical situations and structures using algebraic symbols

Unit 2: Algebra: *Practice Activity 6*

Graph all three lines on the graph beneath each set of equations. The first one is done as an example.

1. $y = 2x + 5$
$y = 3x + 3$
$y = 4x + 3$

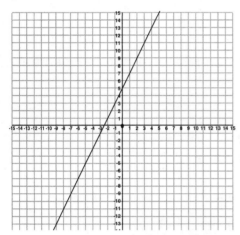

2. $y = x - 8$
$y = 1x + 3$
$y = 3x + 5$

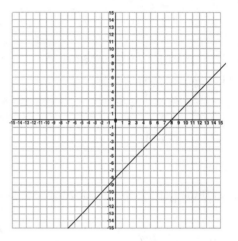

3. $y = 4x - 12$
$y = 1x + 3$
$y = \frac{1}{2}x + 3$

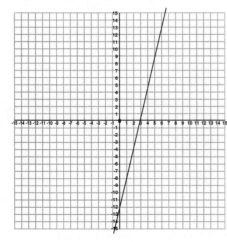

4. $y = -x + 5$
$y = -x + 3$
$y = -2x + 3$

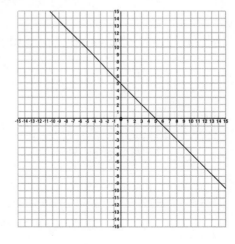

Name: _____ Date: _____

Skill: Representing and analyzing mathematical situations and structures using algebraic symbols

Unit 2: Algebra: *Assessment 2*

Mark the answer that correctly expresses each number sentence.

1. ten less fifteen
   - ○ A. 10 - 15
   - ○ B. 15 - 10
   - ○ C. 10 + 15
   - ○ D. 15 + 10

2. six more than one-half a number
   - ○ A. $\frac{1}{2}x - 6$
   - ○ B. $\frac{1}{2}x + 6$
   - ○ C. $\frac{3}{4} + 6$
   - ○ D. $\frac{1}{2} \cdot 6$

3. the product of eight and four
   - ○ A. 8 x 6
   - ○ B. 8 ÷ 4
   - ○ C. 4 x 4
   - ○ D. 8 x 4

4. the square of a number decreased by three
   - ○ A. $x^2 - 3$
   - ○ B. $x^3 - 4$
   - ○ C. $x^6 - 3$
   - ○ D. $x \cdot 3$

5. Which graph shows solutions to the equation $3x - 0 = 9$?

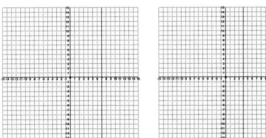 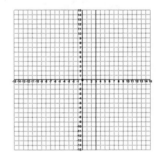 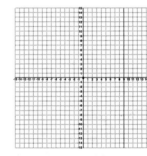

   ○ A.   ○ B.   ○ C.   ○ D.

6. Which graph shows solutions to the equation $2x - 1 = 3$?

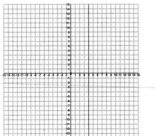 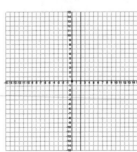 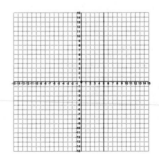 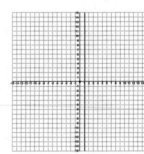

   ○ A.   ○ B.   ○ C.   ○ D.

Name: _____ Date: _____

Unit 2: Algebra: *Assessment 2 (cont.)*

7. Which graph shows solutions to the equation $\frac{1}{2}x + 4 = 5$?

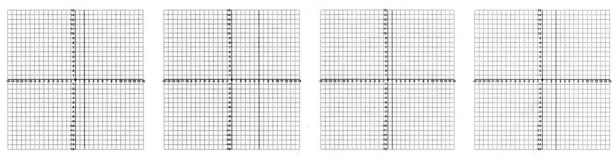

    ◯ A.   ◯ B.   ◯ C.   ◯ D.

8. Which graph shows solutions for the equation $9x - 2 = 12$?

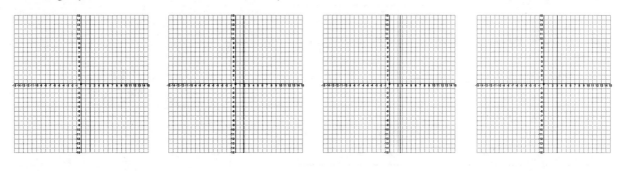

    ◯ A.   ◯ B.   ◯ C.   ◯ D.

Solve for y, given $x = 5$.

9. $y = -3x + 3$
    ◯ A. $y = 12$
    ◯ B. $y = -12$
    ◯ C. $y = 4$
    ◯ D. $y = 6$

Given $x = 2$, solve for y.

10. $y = 4x - 10$
    ◯ A. $y = -2$
    ◯ B. $y = 3$
    ◯ C. $y = -4$
    ◯ D. $y = 6$

Name: _____   Date: _____

Skill: Using mathematical models to represent and understand quantitative relationships

Unit 2: Algebra: *Practice Activity 7*

Solve the following equations.

1. $2 \times 10^2 =$ _____

2. $3 \times 10^8 =$ _____

3. $5 \times 10^6 =$ _____

4. $4 \times 10^4 =$ _____

5. $12 \times 10^3 =$ _____

6. $1.50 \times 10^3 =$ _____

7. $25^4 =$ _____

8. $0.02 \times 10^3 =$ _____

9. $\frac{6}{7} \times \frac{5}{4} =$ _____

10. $\frac{3}{9} \times \frac{1}{2} =$ _____

11. $\frac{3}{4} \times \frac{1}{4} =$ _____

12. $\frac{5}{7} \times \frac{2}{3} =$ _____

13. $-4 \times 8 =$ _____

14. $-3 \times -6 =$ _____

15. $-5 \times 11 =$ _____

WAKE-UP WORD PROBLEM: José makes five deposits at the bank. He deposits the following amounts of money: $102.75, $80.50, $75.75, $89.50, $105.95. What was José's average deposit?

_____

Name: _____ Date: _____

Skill: Using mathematical models to represent and understand quantitative relationships

Unit 2: Algebra: *Practice Activity 8*

Answer the following questions.

1. What is the real number division answer to the division problem 78 divided by 8?

   _____

2. What is the integer division answer for the division problem 78 divided by 8?

   _____

3. A fan's blades rotate 4,500 times per hour. How many times do they rotate per minute?

   _____

4. The Algebraic Definition of Division is, "for any numbers *a* and *b, b* not equal to 0, *a* divided by *b* = *a* times _____."

5. *x/y* = _____

6. What is $\frac{3}{4} \div \frac{1}{3}$? _____

7. What is $6\frac{1}{4} \div 4\frac{3}{4}$? _____

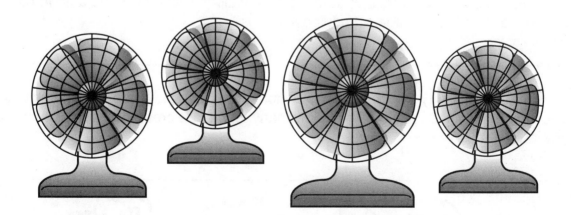

Name: _____   Date: _____

Skill: Using mathematical models to represent and understand quantitative relationships

Unit 2: Algebra: *Practice Activity 9*

Solve each problem.

1. 785 ÷ 16 = _____

2. Tyree wants to calculate the number of minutes in 875 seconds. How many minutes are in 875 seconds?

    _____

3. 397 ÷ 14 = _____

4. Jared measures a piece of cloth for his Halloween costume. The cloth is 1,000 inches. Change this number to feet and inches.

    _____

5. 2,468 ÷ 12 = _____

6. Jeremy buys two hundred and eight pencils to divide between ninety-five back-to-school boxes. Assuming he puts the same number of pencils in each box, how many pencils will he put in each box? Will he have any left over?

    _____

7. A popular restaurant can seat 92 people at a time. They seat people at 6 P.M., 8 P.M., and 9 P.M. Three hundred and eight people try to make reservations for a Saturday night. How many of the people that attempt to make reservations will actually be able to be seated during the restaurant's three scheduled seatings?

    _____

8. Seven hundred eighty-five players sign up for soccer. The players are divided into teams. Each team has fifteen players on it. How many teams are created? How many players, if any, are left over?

Name: _____ Date: _____

Skill: Using mathematical models to represent and understand quantitative relationships

Unit 2: Algebra: *Assessment 3*

Solve each expression and mark the correct answer.

1. 8×10^6
   - ○ A. 8,000,000
   - ○ B. 800,000
   - ○ C. 8,500,000
   - ○ D. 8,400,020

2. 1.75×10^3
   - ○ A. 1,230
   - ○ B. 1,750
   - ○ C. 1,880
   - ○ D. 1,550

3. $\frac{4}{3} \times \frac{1}{2} =$
   - ○ A. $\frac{1}{4}$
   - ○ B. $\frac{1}{2}$
   - ○ C. $\frac{2}{3}$
   - ○ D. $\frac{6}{9}$

4. $\frac{1}{8} \times \frac{5}{6} =$
   - ○ A. $5\frac{6}{8}$
   - ○ B. $\frac{6}{40}$
   - ○ C. $\frac{5}{48}$
   - ○ D. $1\frac{5}{8}$

5. $2,321 \div 14 =$
   - ○ A. 165.79
   - ○ B. 175.89
   - ○ C. 181.25
   - ○ D. 116.75

6. 0.007×10^9
   - ○ A. 7,000,000
   - ○ B. 7,500,000
   - ○ C. 8,000,000
   - ○ D. 9,000,000

7. $1,234 \div 6 =$
   - ○ A. 212.81
   - ○ B. 205.67
   - ○ C. 210.75
   - ○ D. 205.50

8. $4,765 \div 9 =$
   - ○ A. 529.44
   - ○ B. 525.84
   - ○ C. 574.89
   - ○ D. 509.99

9. $-4 \times 12 =$
   - ○ A. -48
   - ○ B. 48
   - ○ C. -54
   - ○ D. 55

10. A moving company is moving 2,876 pounds of boxes. They want to divide the number of pounds as equally as possible between three trucks. About how many pounds will each moving truck move?
    - ○ A. 989 pounds
    - ○ B. 959 pounds
    - ○ C. 917 pounds
    - ○ D. 121 pounds

Name: _____ Date: _____

Skill: Understanding measurable attributes of objects and the units, systems, and processes of measurement

Unit 3: Measurement: *Practice Activity 1*

Just a Tip: One centimeter is smaller than one inch. One millimeter is smaller than one centimeter.

Use your ruler to complete problems 1–10.

1. Draw a line that is $1\frac{1}{8}$ inches in length.

2. Draw a line that is $\frac{3}{4}$ inches in length.

3. Draw a line that is $\frac{1}{8}$ inches in length.

4. Draw a line that is 32 millimeters in length.

5. Draw a line that is 21 millimeters in length.

6. Draw a line that is 18 millimeters in length.

7. Draw a line that is $\frac{3}{4}$ of a centimeter in length.

8. Draw a line that is $\frac{1}{2}$ of a centimeter in length.

9. Draw a line that is $1\frac{1}{2}$ centimeters in length.

10. Draw a line that is $2\frac{1}{4}$ inches in length.

Name: _____ Date: _____

Skill: Understanding measurable attributes of objects and the units, systems, and processes of measurement

Unit 3: Measurement: *Practice Activity 2*

Convert each unit of measurement.

> ***Example:*** 2 pounds = 32 ounces. 2 x 16 = 32

Length:

1. 6 miles = _____ feet

2. 9 yards = _____ feet

3. 12 feet = _____ inches

4. 79,200 feet = _____ miles

Weight:

5. 7 pounds = _____ ounces

6. 10,000 pounds = _____ tons

Capacity:

7. 10 cups = _____ pints

8. 4 quarts = _____ pints

9. 5 gallons = _____ quarts

Converting between systems:

10. 5 pounds = _____ kilograms

11. 15 inches = _____ centimeters

12. 5 kilometers = _____ miles

---

12 inches = 1 foot
3 feet = 1 yard
5,280 feet = 1 mile
16 ounces = 1 pound
2,000 pounds = 1 ton
8 ounces = 1 cup
2 cups = 1 pint
2 pints = 1 quart
4 quarts = 1 gallon

1 inch = 2.54 centimeters
1 pound = 0.3782 kilograms
1 kilometer = 0.6214 miles

Extension Activity: Have students locate some numbers involving measurement in the newspaper. Then have them convert the unit of measurement to another system of measurement.

Name: _____ Date: _____

Skill: Understanding measurable attributes of objects and the units, systems, and processes of measurement

Unit 3: Measurement: *Practice Activity 3*

 Just a Tip: A **right angle** is exactly 90°. An **acute angle** is greater than 0° and less than 90°. An **obtuse angle** is greater than 90° and less than 180°.

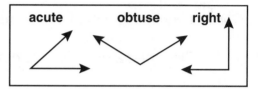

Use your protractor to measure each angle.

Angles:

1. _____    2. _____

3. _____   4. _____

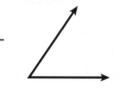

5. _____   6. _____

7. _____

Circle the right angle.

8. A.   B.    C.

Circle the obtuse angle.

9. A.    B.   C.

Circle the acute angle.

10. A.    B.   C.

Name: _____ Date: _____

Skill: Understanding measurable attributes of objects and the units, systems, and processes of measurement

Unit 3: Measurement: *Practice Activity 4*

Just a Tip: Area can be found by multiplying the length of a shape by the width: $A = l \times w$. You can write area measurements with the notation in.^{2}, cm^2, etc.

Find the area of each square.

1. _____ square with one side = 2 centimeters

2. _____ square with one side = 15 feet

3. _____ square with one side = 12 feet

4. _____ square with one side = 4 centimeters

5. _____ square with one side = 6 centimeters

Just a Tip: Volume can be found by multiplying the length times the width times the height of an object: $V = l \times w \times h$. You can write volume measurements with the notation in.^{3}, cm^3, etc.

Find the volume of each cube:

6. _____ cube with an edge = 8 centimeters

7. _____ cube with an edge = 6 millimeters

8. _____ cube with an edge = 4 yards

9. _____ cube with an edge = 5 feet

10. _____ cube with an edge = 10 inches

 **WAKE-UP WORD PROBLEM:** Hannah and Louise want to find the area of a seventy-five foot square. What is the area of the square?

_____

Name: _____ Date: _____

Skill: Understanding measurable attributes of objects and the units, systems, and processes of measurement

Unit 3: Measurement: *Assessment 1*

1. Use your protractor. Which answer shows a 65-degree angle?

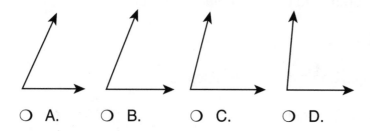

  ○ A.   ○ B.   ○ C.   ○ D.

2. Use your protractor. Which answer shows a 110-degree angle?

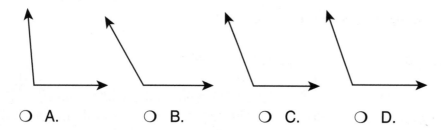

  ○ A.   ○ B.   ○ C.   ○ D.

3. How many yards are in 36 feet?
   ○ A. 18
   ○ B. 12
   ○ C. 16
   ○ D. 14

4. What is the area of the square?
   ○ A. 80 square feet
   ○ B. 81 square feet
   ○ C. 95 square feet
   ○ D. 87 square feet

 9 ft.

5. What is the volume of the cube?
   ○ A. 1,000 cubic yards
   ○ B. 1,500 cubic yards
   ○ C. 1,250 cubic yards
   ○ D. 879 cubic yards

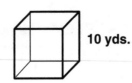 10 yds.

Name: _____ Date: _____

Unit 3: Measurement: *Assessment 1 (cont.)*

6. Use your ruler. Which line is 16 millimeters long?

    ○ A. ▬▬▬▬

    ○ B. ▬▬▬

    ○ C. ▬▬▬

    ○ D. ▬▬▬

7. Which of the following is the best definition of an acute angle?
    ○ A. an angle measuring more than 90 degrees
    ○ B. an angle measuring less than 90 degrees
    ○ C. an angle measuring 90 degrees
    ○ D. an angle measuring 180 degrees

8. How many centimeters are in 20 inches?
    ○ A. 50.80
    ○ B. 55.85
    ○ C. 80.50
    ○ D. 54.87

9. What is the volume of the cube?
    ○ A. 9,007 cubic millimeters
    ○ B. 9,589 cubic millimeters
    ○ C. 9,789 cubic millimeters
    ○ D. 9,261 cubic millimeters

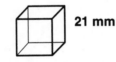

21 mm

10. Use your protractor. Which answer shows a 150-degree angle?

    ○ A.

    ○ B.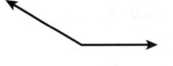

    ○ C.

    ○ D.

Name: _____ Date: _____

Review of Four Previously Taught NCTM Standards

- **Understanding patterns, relations, and functions**

- **Representing and analyzing mathematical situations and structures using algebraic structures**

- **Using mathematical models to represent and understand quantitative relationships**

- **Understanding measurable attributes of objects and the units, systems, and processes of measurement**

1. Which graph shows the equation $x - y = 7$?

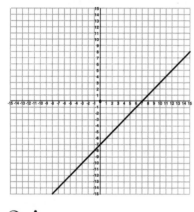 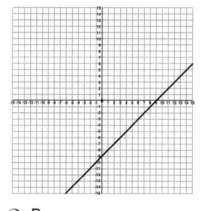 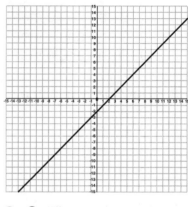

    ○ A.   ○ B.   ○ C.

Evaluate each expression.

2. eight more than a number divided by two
   - ○ A. $x \cdot 2 + 8$
   - ○ B. $x/2 + 8$
   - ○ C. $8 + 2 - x$
   - ○ D. $x + 8 - 2$

3. the product of nine and eleven
   - ○ A. 78
   - ○ B. 98
   - ○ C. 102
   - ○ D. 99

4. 8×10^6
   - ○ A. 8,000,000
   - ○ B. 8,500,000
   - ○ C. 7,000,000
   - ○ D. 7,900,000

5. $\frac{4}{5} \times \frac{5}{9} =$
   - ○ A. $\frac{3}{4}$
   - ○ B. $\frac{1}{2}$
   - ○ C. $\frac{5}{7}$
   - ○ D. $\frac{4}{9}$

6. $987 \div 12 =$
   - ○ A. 82.25
   - ○ B. 87.98
   - ○ C. 85.50
   - ○ D. 81.98

Name: _____ Date: _____

Review of Four Previously Taught NCTM Standards (cont.)

7. Use your ruler. Which line is 12 millimeters in length?

    ○ A. ▬

    ○ B. ▬▬

    ○ C. ▬▬

    ○ D. ▬

8. Use your protractor. Which angle measures 108 degrees?

    ○ A.   ○ B.

    ○ C.   ○ D.

9. Find the area of the square.
    ○ A. 48 square inches
    ○ B. 49 square inches
    ○ C. 51 square inches
    ○ D. 54 square inches

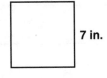

7 in.

10. What is the volume of the cube?
    ○ A. 46.24 cubic centimeters
    ○ B. 20.4 cubic centimeters
    ○ C. 40.8 cubic centimeters
    ○ D. 314.432 cubic centimeters

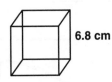

6.8 cm

Name: _____ Date: _____

Skill: Applying appropriate techniques, tools, and formulas to determine measurements

Unit 3: Measurement: *Practice Activity 5*

Just a Tip: The **circumference** is the distance around a circle. To find the circumference of a circle, multiply the **diameter** by **pi** (3.1416): $C = \pi d$. You can also multiply the **radius** times 2 to get the diameter and then multiply by pi: $C = 2\pi r$.

Write the equation to find each circumference, and then solve the equation.

1. diameter = 4.2 centimeters _____

2. radius = 6 centimeters _____

3. radius = 5 centimeters _____

4. diameter = 3.4 millimeters _____

5. radius = 4.1 millimeters _____

Find the circumference to the nearest tenth.

6. diameter = 9.2 centimeters _____

7. radius = 1.4 millimeters _____

8. radius = 7 feet _____

9. diameter = 8 feet _____

10. diameter = 5.1 inches _____

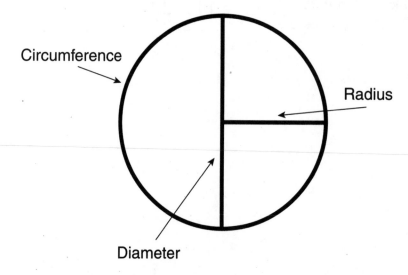

Name: _____ Date: _____

Skill: Applying appropriate techniques, tools, and formulas to determine measurements

Unit 3: Measurement: *Practice Activity 6*

Just a Tip: To find the **surface area** of a cylinder, you can break the problem down into three parts: finding the area of the top base, the bottom base, and the curved surface of the cylinder. To find the area of the bases, just use the formula to find the area of a circle: $A = \pi r^2$ and $r = \frac{1}{2}d$. To find the area of the curved surface, take the circumference of one of the bases and multiply it times the height of the cylinder. Then, add all three areas together to get the total surface area.

Example: Cylinder with a base radius of 1.5 inches and a height of 8 inches

Area of base = 3.1416 x 1.5² = 7.0686 in.²
Circumference of base = (2 x 1.5) x 3.1416 = 9.4248 in.²
Area of curved side = 9.4248 x 8 = 75.3984 in.²
Surface area = 7.0686 + 7.0686 + 75.3984 = 89.5356 in.²

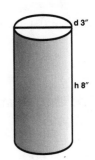

Find the surface area of the cylinders.

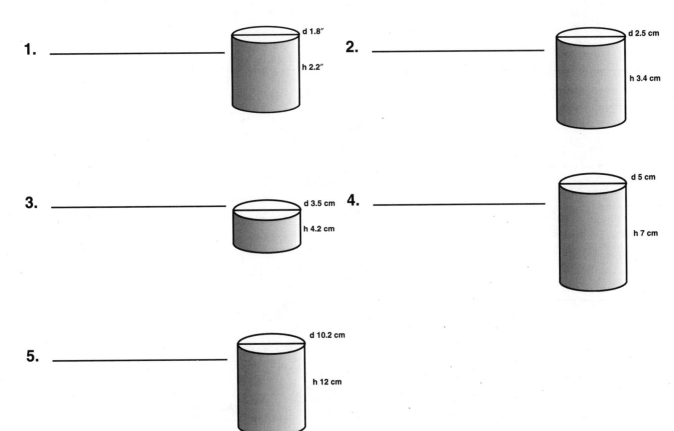

1. _____   d 1.8″   h 2.2″

2. _____   d 2.5 cm   h 3.4 cm

3. _____   d 3.5 cm   h 4.2 cm

4. _____   d 5 cm   h 7 cm

5. _____   d 10.2 cm   h 12 cm

Name: _____ Date: _____

Skill: Applying appropriate techniques, tools, and formulas to determine measurements

Unit 3: Measurement: *Practice Activity 7*

 **Just a Tip:** The volume of a solid can be found by multiplying the length times the width times the height: $V = l \times w \times h$. To find the volume of a cylinder, multiply the square of the radius of the base by pi, and then multiply by the height of the cylinder: $V = (\pi r^2)h$. Remember, pi = 3.1416.

Examples: To find the volume of a cylinder with a base radius of 3 inches and a height of 7 inches, multiply: $(3.1416 \times 3^2) \times 7 = 197.9208$ cubic inches.

To find the volume of a rectangular prism with a base length of 4 inches, a base width of 6 inches, and a height of 9 inches, multiply: $4 \times 6 \times 9 = 216$ cubic inches.

Find the volume of each solid. You can write the volume measurement with the notation in.³, cm³, etc.

1. _____

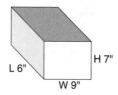

L 6" W 9" H 7"

2. _____

r 7 cm H 15 cm

3. _____

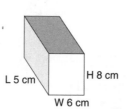

L 5 cm W 6 cm H 8 cm

4. _____

r 9" H 3"

5. _____

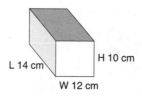

L 14 cm W 12 cm H 10 cm

Name: _____ Date: _____

Skill: Applying appropriate techniques, tools, and formulas to determine measurements

Unit 3: Measurement: *Practice Activity 8*

Just a Tip: Find **area** by multiplying the length times the width: $A = l \times w$. To find the area of a triangle, multiply one-half the base times the height: $A = \frac{1}{2}b \times h$.

Find the area of each rectangle. You can write the area measurement with the notation in.², cm², etc.

1.   length = 3.9 centimeters, width = 5.2 centimeters _____

2.   length = $4\frac{1}{8}$ inches, width = $5\frac{1}{2}$ inches _____

3.   length = 18 feet, width = 21 feet _____

4.   length = 9 centimeters, width = 10.5 centimeters _____

Find the area of each triangle.

5.   base = 4 centimeters, height = 9.5 centimeters _____

6.   base = 11 inches, height = 5.4 inches _____

7.   base = 8 feet, height = 10 feet _____

8.   base = 15 inches, height = 12 inches _____

Just a Tip: To find the **perimeter** of a shape, add the lengths of all sides of the shape.

Find the perimeter of each irregular shape.

9.   _____

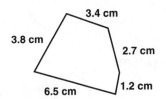

3.4 cm

3.8 cm

2.7 cm

1.2 cm

6.5 cm

10.   _____

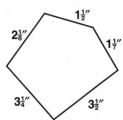

$1\frac{1}{2}''$

$2\frac{1}{8}''$

$1\frac{1}{7}''$

$3\frac{1}{4}''$

$3\frac{1}{2}''$

Extension Activity: Pick an object in your classroom and/or at home. Find the area of the object(s).

Name: _____ Date: _____

Skill: Applying appropriate techniques, tools, and formulas to determine measurements

Unit 3: Measurement: *Assessment 2*

1. Which formula should be used to find the circumference of the circle?
   - ○ A. πd
   - ○ B. πa
   - ○ C. $a \times h$
   - ○ D. $b \times h$

   D 6.2 cm

2. Find the surface area of the cylinder.
   - ○ A. 16.876 in.²
   - ○ B. 16.727 in.²
   - ○ C. 18.098 in.²
   - ○ D. 18.008 in.²

   D 1.5"
   H 2.8"

3. Find the surface area of the cylinder.
   - ○ A. 61.26 in.²
   - ○ B. 102.48 in.²
   - ○ C. 150.80 in.²
   - ○ D. 94.25 in.²

   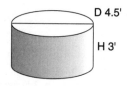
   r 3"
   H 5"

4. Find the volume of the cylinder.
   - ○ A. 477.89 ft.³
   - ○ B. 4.071 ft.³
   - ○ C. 45.89 ft.³
   - ○ D. 47.71 ft.³

   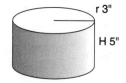
   D 4.5'
   H 3'

5. What is the circumference of the circle?
   - ○ A. 58.09 in.
   - ○ B. 56.55 in.
   - ○ C. 55.22 in.
   - ○ D. 57.865 in.

   r 9"

6. Find the volume of the rectangular prism.
   - ○ A. 831.25 in.³
   - ○ B. 856.75 in.⁵
   - ○ C. 876.9 in.
   - ○ D. 908.76 in.³

   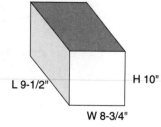
   L 9-1/2"
   H 10"
   W 8-3/4"

Name: _____ Date: _____

Unit 3: Measurement: Assessment 2 (cont.)

7. Find the area of the right triangle.
- ○ A. 15.54 in.²
- ○ B. 7.9 in.²
- ○ C. 15.8 in.²
- ○ D. 7.77 in.²

4.2″

3.7″

8. Find the area of the right triangle.
- ○ A. 10.8 ft.²
- ○ B. 5.4 ft.²
- ○ C. 3.465 ft.²
- ○ D. 6.93 ft.²

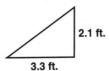

2.1 ft.

3.3 ft.

9. What is the circumference of the circle?
- ○ A. 35.95 mm
- ○ B. 36.44 mm
- ○ C. 45.75 mm
- ○ D. 32.12 mm

r 5.8 mm

10. Find the area of the rectangle.
- ○ A. 83.3 cm
- ○ B. 83.3 cm²
- ○ C. 89.7 cm²
- ○ D. 89.7 cm

8.5 cm

9.8 cm

Name: _____ Date: _____

Skill: Analyzing characteristics and properties of two- and three-dimensional geometric shapes and developing mathematical arguments about geometric relationships

Unit 4: Geometry: *Practice Activity 1*

Simplify. You may use a calculator. Round answers to the nearest hundredth.

1. $\sqrt{49}$ _____

2. $\sqrt{56}$ _____

3. $\sqrt{64}$ _____

4. $\sqrt{197 - 106}$ _____

5. $\sqrt{36}$ _____

6. $\sqrt{48}$ _____

7. $\sqrt{212 - 185}$ _____

8. $\sqrt{125}$ _____

9. $\sqrt{4 + 5}$ _____

10. $\sqrt{28}$ _____

WAKE-UP WORD PROBLEM: Three friends visit the school book fair together. They spend totals of $14.45, $18.75, and $15.50. What was the average amount of money that the three friends spent?

_____

Name: _____ Date: _____

Skill: Analyzing characteristics and properties of two- and three-dimensional geometric shapes and developing mathematical arguments about geometric relationships

Unit 4: Geometry: *Practice Activity 2*

Write one complete sentence describing each shape.

1. cylinder: _____

_____

2. rectangular cube: _____

_____

3. circle: _____

_____

4. sphere: _____

_____

5. cube: _____

_____

6. triangular prism: _____

_____

7. rectangular prism: _____

_____

8. pyramid: _____

_____

9. cone: _____

_____

10. equilateral triangle: _____

_____

Name: _____ Date: _____

Skill: Analyzing characteristics and properties of two- and three-dimensional geometric shapes and developing mathematical arguments about geometric relationships

Unit 4: Geometry: *Practice Activity 3*

Just a Tip: The Pythagorean Theorem: Let the legs of a right triangle have lengths *a* and *b*. Let the hypotenuse have length *c*. Then $a^2 + b^2 = c^2$. So, if you know the lengths of two legs of a triangle, you can find the other length.

> ***Examples:***
>
> $a = 6$, $b = 9$ To find *c*: $6^2 + 9^2 = 117$. The square root of 117 is 10.82, so $c = 10.82$.
>
> $b = 8$, $c = 15$ To find *a*: $c^2 = 225$, $c^2 - b^2 = a^2$, so $225 - 64 = 161$. The square root of 161 is 12.69, so $a = 12.69$.

Find the missing side of each right triangle. Round your answers to the nearest hundredth.

1. *c* = _____

32

16

2. *a* = _____

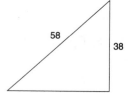

58

38

3. *c* = _____

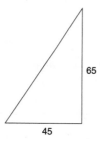

65

45

4. *a* = _____

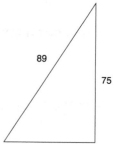

89

75

5. *a* = _____

132

125

Name: _____ Date: _____

Skill: Analyzing characteristics and properties of two- and three-dimensional geometric shapes and developing mathematical arguments about geometric relationships

Unit 4: Geometry: *Assessment 1*

1. Which answer shows a triangular prism?

    ○ A. 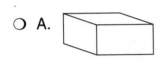 ○ B.  ○ C. 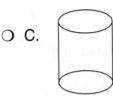 ○ D.

2. Solve. $\sqrt{58}$
    ○ A. 7.62
    ○ B. 8.95
    ○ C. 7.88
    ○ D. 8.04

3. Find the missing side of the right triangle. $a = 79$, $b = 85$
    ○ A. $c = 116.04$
    ○ B. $c = 118.08$
    ○ C. $c = 102.65$
    ○ D. $c = 124.7$

4. Find the missing side of the triangle. leg 1 = 65, hypotenuse = 101
    ○ A. $b = 75.2$
    ○ B. $b = 75.90$
    ○ C. $b = 77.30$
    ○ D. $b = 74.5$

5. The Pythagorean Theorem =
    ○ A. $a^2 + b^2 = c^2$
    ○ B. $a - b + c^2$
    ○ C. $a^2 + b^2$
    ○ D. $a^2 - b^2 = c^2$

6. Which answer shows a cylinder?

    ○ A. 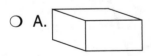 ○ B.   ○ C.   ○ D.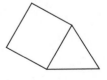

Name: _____ Date: _____

Unit 4: Geometry: *Assessment 1 (cont.)*

7. Find the missing side of the right triangle. $a = 108$, $c = 128$
   - ○ A. $b = 68.70$
   - ○ B. $b = 75.5$
   - ○ C. $b = 43.9$
   - ○ D. $b = 67.80$

8. Which of the following statements is true?
   - ○ A. The Pythagorean Theorem works for all triangles.
   - ○ B. The Pythagorean Theorem works only for right triangles.
   - ○ C. The Pythagorean Theorem works for all shapes.
   - ○ D. The Pythagorean Theorem is helpful when you are trying to find the circumference of a circle.

9. Find the missing side of the right triangle. $a = 64$, $b = 98$
   - ○ A. $c = 102.38$
   - ○ B. $c = 127.50$
   - ○ C. $c = 117.05$
   - ○ D. $c = 171.05$

10. Solve. $\sqrt{95 - 15}$
    - ○ A. ± 8.05
    - ○ B. ± 5.94
    - ○ C. ± 8.97
    - ○ D. ± 8.94

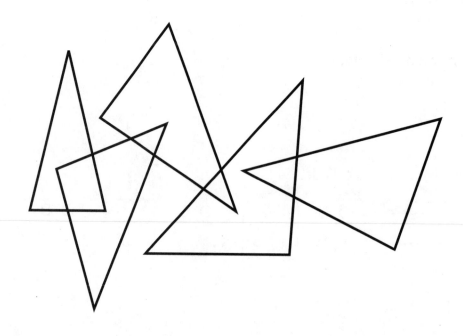

Name: _____ Date: _____

Skill: Specifying locations and describing spatial relationships using coordinate geometry and other representational systems

Unit 4: Geometry: *Practice Activity 4*

Just a Tip: The coordinate graph is frequently preferred because it is easier to read than a table. The first number in a coordinate pair is the **x-axis coordinate**. The second number is the **y-axis coordinate**.

Example: The coordinate pair (-2,5) is found by moving two spaces to the left on the *x*-axis and then five spaces up on the *y*-axis. It is graphed as point **P** on the coordinate graph.

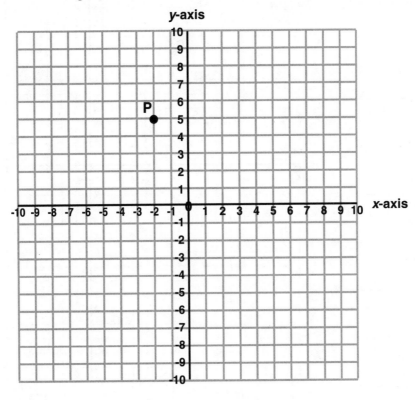

Graph the following points on the coordinate graph above.

A. (-8,1)   **F.** (-4,2)

B. (6,5)   **G.** (5,5)

C. (9,2)   **H.** (10,-9)

D. (-7,5)   **I.** (6,-6)

E. (0,8)   **J.** (10,2)

51

Name: _____ Date: _____

Skill: Specifying locations and describing spatial relationships using coordinate geometry and other representational systems

Unit 4: Geometry: *Practice Activity 5*

Write the coordinate pair for each point.

1. B = _____

2. C = _____

3. F = _____

4. G = _____

5. A = _____

6. Q = _____

7. M = _____

8. L = _____

9. R = _____

10. S = _____

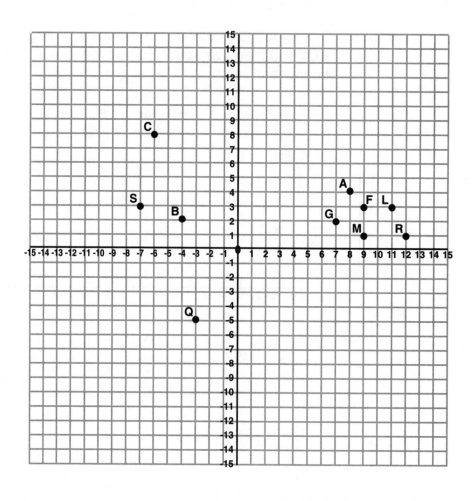

Extension Activity: Have students draw a simple picture on graph paper. Then have the students plot the coordinates that could be used to recreate the picture.

Name: _____ Date: _____

Skill: Specifying locations and describing spatial relationships using coordinate geometry and other representational systems

Unit 4: Geometry: *Practice Activity 6*

Graph each point on the graph. Then, connect the points in order.

1. (12,-1)

2. (9,8)

3. (-6,6)

4. (9,0)

5. (5,2)

6. (-7,1)

7. (6,3)

8. (10,7)

9. (-7,10)

10. (-2,8)

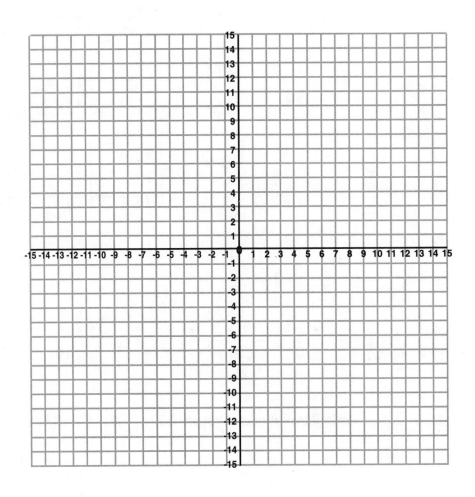

WAKE-UP WORD PROBLEM: Tonya has $586.50. She divides the money equally between her savings and checking accounts. How much money does she put in each account?

_____

Name: _____ Date: _____

Skill: Specifying locations and describing spatial relationships using coordinate geometry and other representational systems

Unit 4: Geometry: *Assessment 2*

Use the coordinate graph pictured below to answer questions 1–5.

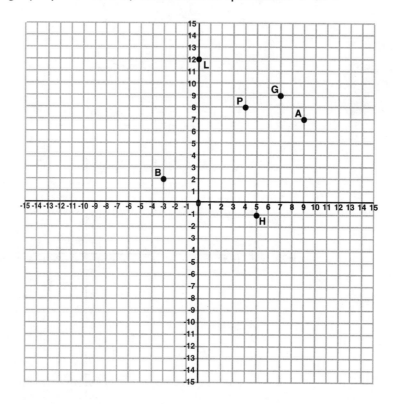

1. Point ___ is located at coordinates (9,7).
   - ○ A. A
   - ○ B. B
   - ○ C. G
   - ○ D. H

2. On which coordinates is point G located?
   - ○ A. (9,7)
   - ○ B. (7,9)
   - ○ C. (-3,2)
   - ○ D. (0,12)

3. On which coordinates is point L located?
   - ○ A. (4,8)
   - ○ B. (-3,2)
   - ○ C. (9,7)
   - ○ D. (0,12)

4. On which coordinates is point P located?
   - ○ A. (9,7)
   - ○ B. (0,12)
   - ○ C. (4,8)
   - ○ D. (5,-1)

5. Point ___ is located at coordinates (5,-1).
   - ○ A. H
   - ○ B. L
   - ○ C. P
   - ○ D. G

Name: _____ Date: _____

Unit 4: Geometry: *Assessment 2 (cont.)*

Use the coordinate graph below to answer questions 6–10.

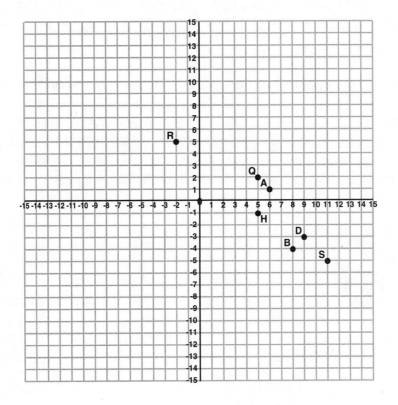

6. Point ___ is located at coordinates (-2,5).
   - ○ A. D
   - ○ B. S
   - ○ C. B
   - ○ D. R

7. On which coordinates is point B located?
   - ○ A. (6,1)
   - ○ B. (8,-4)
   - ○ C. (-2,5)
   - ○ D. (5,2)

8. On which coordinates is point A located?
   - ○ A. (1,6)
   - ○ B. (8,-4)
   - ○ C. (6,1)
   - ○ D. (9,-3)

9. Point ___ is located at coordinates (11,-5).
   - ○ A. D
   - ○ B. R
   - ○ C. Q
   - ○ D. S

10. On which coordinates is point Q located?
   - ○ A. (5,2)
   - ○ B. (6,1)
   - ○ C. (11,-5)
   - ○ D. (-2,5)

55

Name: _____ Date: _____

Skill: Applying transformations and using symmetry to analyze mathematical situations

Unit 4: Geometry: *Practice Activity 7*

Just a Tip: Adding the same number to the coordinates of the points in a figure results in a translation image.

Which of the following sets of points represents a translation of the original triangle?

1. Triangle PQR = (2,3), (3,7), (4,9)
   ○ A. (7,1), (8,5), (9,7)
   ○ B. (7,1), (8,4), (9,5)
   ○ C. (7,1), (8,5), (9,3)

2. Triangle ABC = (6,5), (6,6), 9,5)
   ○ A. (8,2), (8,3), (11,2)
   ○ B. (8,4), (8,6), (7,2)
   ○ C. (8,6), (8,3), (11,2)

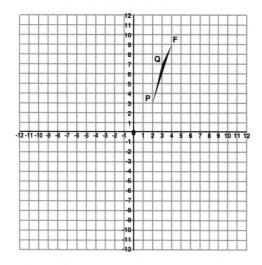

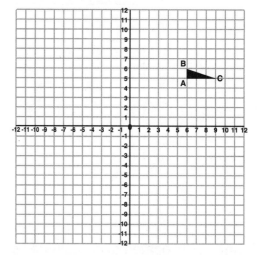

3. Triangle GHI = (10,5), (7,6), (11,5)
   ○ A. (5,1), (2,2), (6,2)
   ○ B. (5,4), (3,7), (6,1)
   ○ C. (5,1), (2,2), (6,1)

4. Triangle ADE = (7,2), (6,1), (9,7)
   ○ A. (4,8), (3,7), (6,12)
   ○ B. (4,8), (3,7), (6,13)
   ○ C. (5,8), (3,9), (6,11)

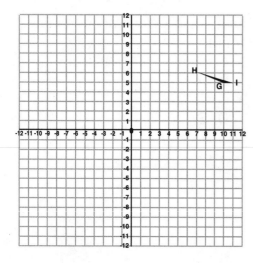

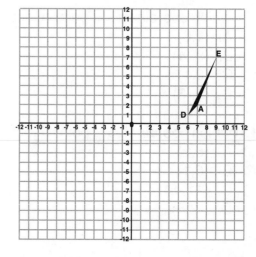

56

Name: _____ Date: _____

Skill: Applying transformations and using symmetry to analyze mathematical situations

Unit 4: Geometry: *Practice Activity 8*

Just a Tip: A **reflection** is a mirror image.

> **Example:** Draw the reflection image of T over line B.

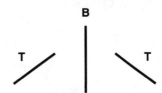

Trace each drawing. Then, draw a reflection image of the given figure over the line.

1.

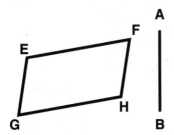

2.

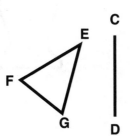

3.

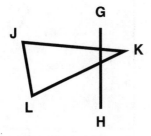

Name: _____ Date: _____

Skill: Applying transformations and using symmetry to analyze mathematical situations

Unit 4: Geometry: *Practice Activity 9*

Just a Tip: A line of **symmetry** is a line that divides a figure in half, with each half being a mirror image of the other.

Draw all lines of symmetry for each figure.

1.

2.

3.

4.

5.

6.

Extension Activity: Ask students to create their own wallpaper. They will be creating a tessellation. A **tessellation** is a repeating pattern. Give each student a piece of construction paper. Have students create a design they like, and then make reflections of the figure so they create a wallpaper "sample" they can share with their classmates.

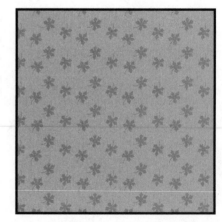

58

Name: _____ Date: _____

Skill: Applying transformations and using symmetry to analyze mathematical situations

Unit 4: Geometry: *Practice Activity 10*

Just a Tip: A **congruent** figure is one that is the same size and shape as another.

> *Example:* The two quadrilaterals shown on the grid are congruent.

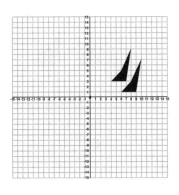

Draw congruent figures for each shape shown.

1.

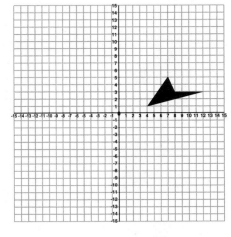

2.

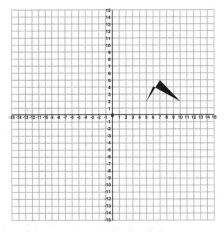

3.

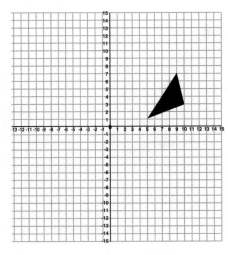

WAKE-UP WORD PROBLEM: The attendance at the opening football game for a popular professional team is 57,987. About one-third of the people in attendance are less than eighteen years old. How many of the people at the game are over eighteen years old?

_____

_____

59

Name: _____ Date: _____

Skill: Applying transformations and using symmetry to analyze mathematical situations

Unit 4: Geometry: *Assessment 3*

1. Which graph shows a reflection of triangle ABC?

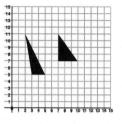　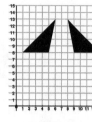　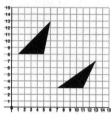　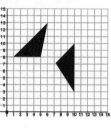

○ A.　　　　　○ B.　　　　　○ C.　　　　　○ D.

2. Which graph shows a translation of triangle EFG?

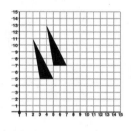　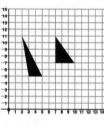　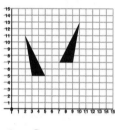　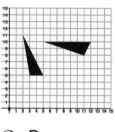

○ A.　　　　　○ B.　　　　　○ C.　　　　　○ D.

3. Which answer shows a reflection image of the letter "G" over line A?

○ A.　　　　　○ B.　　　　　○ C.　　　　　○ D.

4. Which answer shows a reflection image of letter "D" over line C?

　　　D | D

○ A.　　　　　○ B.　　　　　○ C.　　　　　○ D.

5. How many lines of symmetry does the star have?
　　○ A. 8
　　○ B. 12
　　○ C. 4
　　○ D. 6

Name: _____ Date: _____

Unit 4: Geometry: *Assessment 3 (cont.)*

6. How many lines of symmetry does the camera have?
   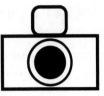
   - ○ A. 2
   - ○ B. 1
   - ○ C. 3
   - ○ D. 0

7. How many lines of symmetry does the parallelogram have?
   - ○ A. 0
   - ○ B. 1
   - ○ C. 2
   - ○ D. 3
   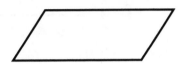

8. Which graph shows two congruent figures?

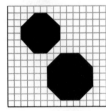 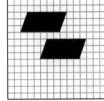 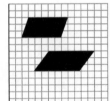 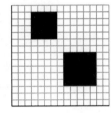

   ○ A. 　　　 ○ B. 　　　 ○ C. 　　　 ○ D.

9. Which set of points describes a triangle that is congruent to one described by points:
   A (5,6), B (9,3), C (4,2)?
   - ○ A. (8,5), (12,2), (7,2)
   - ○ B. (5,3), (2,1), (9,8)
   - ○ C. (5,5), (7,8), (2,2)
   - ○ D. (8,4), (12,1), (7,0)

10. Which set of points describes a triangle that is NOT congruent to triangle ABC at
    A (0,0), B (2,2), C (3,-1)?
    - ○ A. (3,3), (4,4), (6,2)
    - ○ B. (4,4), (6,6), (7,3)
    - ○ C. (3,1), (5,3), (6,0)
    - ○ D. (-2,0), (0,2), (1,-1)

Name: _____ Date: _____

Skill: Using visualization, spatial reasoning, and geometric modeling to solve problems

Unit 4: Geometry: *Practice Activity 11*

Just a Tip: To find the **volume of a sphere**, multipy the cube of the radius by pi (3.1416), then multiply by 4, and then divide by 3. $V = (\pi r^3) \times 4 \div 3$

Find the volume of each sphere.

1. _____
r = 8 cm

2. _____
r = 3.5"

3. _____
r = 5"

4. _____
r = 9 cm

5. _____
r = 2.5"

Find the volume of each rectangular solid. Remember, for a rectangular solid $V = l \times w \times h$.

6. _____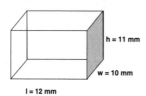
h = 11 mm
w = 10 mm
l = 12 mm

7. _____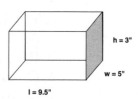
h = 3"
w = 5"
l = 9.5"

8. _____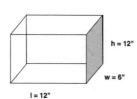
h = 12"
w = 6"
l = 12"

9. _____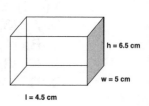
h = 6.5 cm
w = 5 cm
l = 4.5 cm

10. _____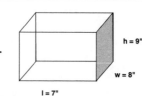
h = 9"
w = 8"
l = 7"

Name: _____ Date: _____

Skill: Using visualization, spatial reasoning, and geometric modeling to solve problems

Unit 4: Geometry: *Practice Activity 12*

Teacher Note: Graph paper should be provided.

Draw each shape on the graph paper provided.

1. a square with one side measuring 2 centimeters

2. a rectangle with length = 4 inches and width = $5\frac{1}{4}$ inches

3. a quadrilateral with one side = $2\frac{1}{2}$ centimeters

4. a triangle with angles 69°, 72°, 39°

5. a triangle with angles 79°, 85°, 16°

Using your protractor, draw each angle in the space below.

6. Draw an angle measuring 87°.

7. Draw an angle measuring 99°.

8. Draw an angle measuring 108°.

9. Draw an angle measuring 178°.

10. Draw an angle measuring 121°.

WAKE-UP WORD PROBLEM: Larry spends $217.50 on birthday presents during the year. His older brother, Henry, spends four times as much money on birthday presents. How much money does Henry spend?

Name: _____ Date: _____

Skill: Using visualization, spatial reasoning, and geometric modeling to solve problems

Unit 4: Geometry: *Assessment 4*

Find the volume of each sphere at the right.

1. ○ A. *V* = 381.70 cubic cm
   ○ B. *V* = 385.40 cubic cm
   ○ C. *V* = 218.70 cubic cm
   ○ D. *V* = 327.95 cubic cm

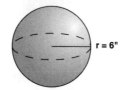

2. ○ A. *V* = 914.85 cubic inches
   ○ B. *V* = 980.75 cubic inches
   ○ C. *V* = 904.78 cubic inches
   ○ D. *V* = 918.74 cubic inches

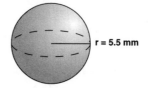

3. ○ A. *V* = 695.72 cubic millimeters
   ○ B. *V* = 785.40 cubic millimeters
   ○ C. *V* = 698.79 cubic millimeters
   ○ D. *V* = 696.91 cubic millimeters

4. Use your protractor. Which angle measures 93 degrees?

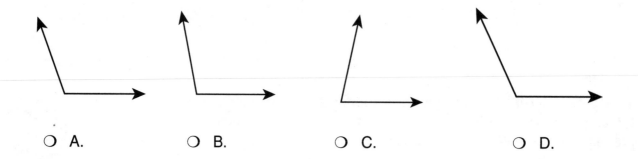

   ○ A.   ○ B.   ○ C.   ○ D.

5. Use your protractor. Which angle measures 101 degrees?

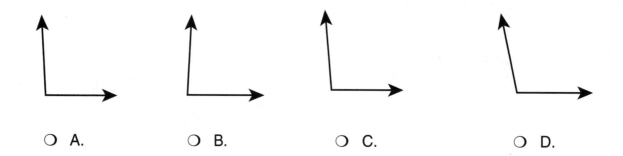

   ○ A.   ○ B.   ○ C.   ○ D.

Name: _____ Date: _____

Unit 4: Geometry: *Assessment 4 (cont.)*

6. Use your protractor. Which angle measures 132 degrees?

○ A.

○ B.

○ C.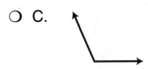

○ D.

7. Which answer shows an acute angle?

○ A.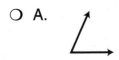

○ B.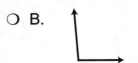

○ C.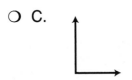

○ D.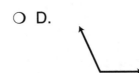

8. Which answer shows a right angle?

○ A.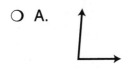

○ B.

○ C.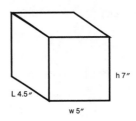

○ D.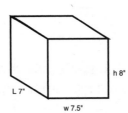

9. Find the volume of the rectangular solid.
   ○ A. 151.2 cubic inches
   ○ B. 157.5 cubic inches
   ○ C. 102.1 cubic inches
   ○ D. 97.8 cubic inches

h 7″
L 4.5″
w 5″

10. Find the volume of the rectangular solid.
    ○ A. 420 cubic inches
    ○ B. 425 cubic inches
    ○ C. 427 cubic inches
    ○ D. 138 cubic inches

h 8″
L 7″
w 7.5″

Name: _____ Date: _____

Skill: Formulating questions that can be addressed with data and collecting, organizing, and displaying relevant data to answer them

Unit 5: Data Analysis and Probability: *Practice Activity 1*

Just a Tip: A **circle graph** or **pie graph** helps you to easily see people's preferences. The circle is divided into fractions of the whole, so comparisons can be made.

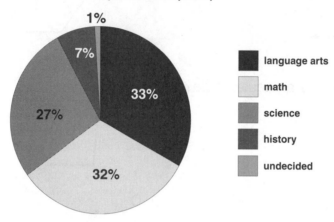

Students' Favorite Subject at Casis Middle School
(350 students polled)

Look at the circle graph. Then answer the five questions about the circle graph.

1. Based on the information in the circle graph, about how many students like science best?

   _____

2. Based on the information in the circle graph, about how many students like math best?

   _____

3. Based on the information in the circle graph, about how many students like language arts best?

   _____

4. Based on the information in the circle graph, about how many students like history best?

   _____

5. Write down two equations you would use to determine the number of students who do not like math best.

   _____

   _____

Extension Activity: Have students poll their own classmates about their favorite subjects. Then have students create a circle graph representing this information.

Name: _____ Date: _____

Skill: Formulating questions that can be addressed with data and collecting, organizing, and displaying relevant data to answer them

Unit 5: Data Analysis and Probability: *Practice Activity 2*

Favorite Flavors
(500 ice cream lovers polled)

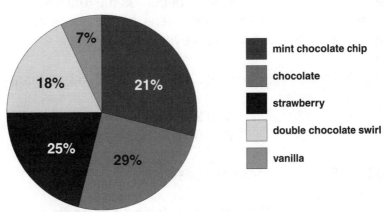

mint chocolate chip

chocolate

strawberry

double chocolate swirl

vanilla

Look at the circle graph. Then answer questions 1–8.

1. Based on the information in the circle graph, how many students like strawberry ice cream best? _____

2. Based on the information in the circle graph, how many students like double chocolate swirl best? _____

3. Based on the information in the circle graph, how many total students like vanilla, chocolate, and strawberry best? _____

4. Based on the information in the circle graph, how many students like mint chocolate chip and double chocolate swirl best? _____

5. How many students' opinions are represented on the circle graph? _____

6. What fraction could you use to represent the number of students who like mint chocolate chip ice cream best? _____

7. What fraction could you use to represent the number of students who like strawberry ice cream best? _____

8. Based on the information in the circle graph, how many students like mint chocolate chip ice cream best? _____

Name: _____ Date: _____

Skill: Formulating questions that can be addressed with data and collecting, organizing, and displaying relevant data to answer them

Unit 5: Data Analysis and Probability: *Practice Activity 3*

Just a Tip: In a Stem and Leaf Plot, the first number in each value becomes the stem on the left side of the plot. The last number becomes the leaf on the right side of the plot. In this way, numbers with the same tens or hundreds digits can be grouped together without rewriting those digits every time.

> ***Example:*** The numbers {42, 48, 65, 42, 49, 66, 60, 47, 63, 68} can be written in a Stem and Leaf Plot as:
>
> 4 | 2 2 7 8 9
> 6 | 0 3 5 6 8

Read the Stem and Leaf Plot. Then answer questions 1–4.

Leslie's Math Grades during Fall Term

6 | 8
7 | 5   7
8 | 1   5   7
9 | 0   4

Key: 6 | 8 = 68

1. How many math grades did Leslie have for the fall term? _____

2. What was the range of Leslie's math scores? _____

3. What was the mode of Leslie's math scores? _____

4. Based on all of Leslie's grades during the fall term, what was Leslie's average in math?

_____

5. On your own paper, make a Stem and Leaf Plot showing your grades in your favorite subject. Write three problems to go along with your Stem and Leaf Plot. Then exchange Stem and Leaf Plots with a friend and solve the questions.

Name: _____ Date: _____

Skill: Formulating questions that can be addressed with data and collecting, organizing, and displaying relevant data to answer them

Unit 5: Data Analysis and Probability: *Practice Activity 4*

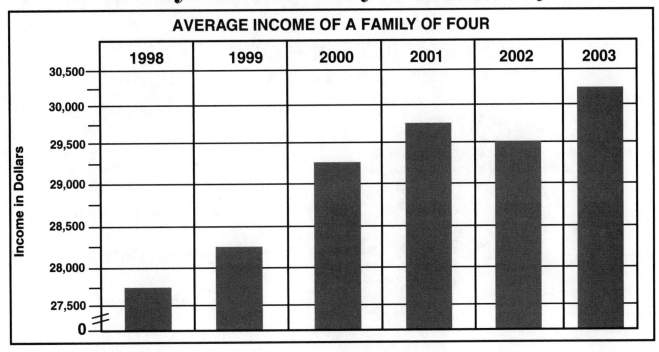

Read the bar graph. Then answer the following questions.

1. How much less was the median income in 1999 than in 2003? _____

2. If the median income for 2004 is 3% more than the median income for 2003, then what is the median income for 2004?

_____

3. What was the average median income for 1998, 1999, and 2000? _____

4. What was the average median income for all six years listed on the bar graph? _____

5. Make an assumption about the information in the graph. _____

_____

_____

6. On your own paper, make a bar graph using the information from the table. Then, write three questions to go along with your bar graph.

Amount of Time Sandy Spent at Work					
Monday	Tuesday	Wednesday	Thursday	Friday	Saturday
6 hours	9 hours	8 hours	10 hours	5 hours	8 hours

Name: _____ Date: _____

Skill: Formulating questions that can be addressed with data and collecting, organizing, and displaying relevant data to answer them

Unit 5: Data Analysis and Probability: *Practice Activity 5*

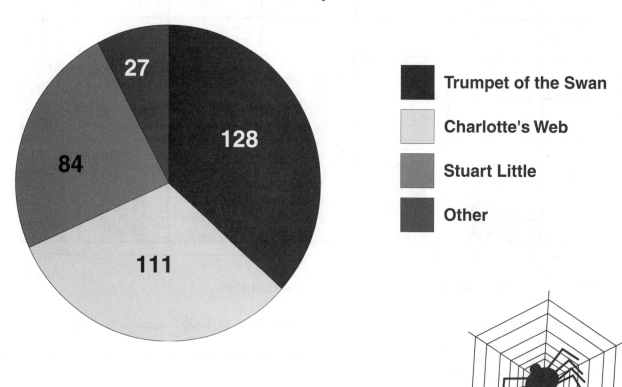

Favorite Book Titles of E.B. White
Based on 350 students polled

Read the circle graph. Then answer questions 1–5.

1. How many students liked *Trumpet of the Swan* best? _____

2. How many students liked *Charlotte's Web* best? _____

3. How many students liked *Stuart Little* best? _____

4. How many students liked another E.B. White book best? _____

5. How many students selected *Charlotte's Web* or *Stuart Little* as their favorite title?

_____

70

Name: _____ Date: _____

Skill: Formulating questions that can be addressed with data and collecting, organizing, and displaying relevant data to answer them

Unit 5: Data Analysis and Probability: *Practice Activity 6*

Average Amount Spent Going Out for Dinner
Based on a poll of 150 seventh graders

34%=less than $5

21%=$5-$7

30%=$8-$10

15%=more than $10

Using the circle graph above, answer the following questions.

1. How many seventh graders spent $5–$7 on dinner? _____

2. How many seventh graders spent more than $10 on dinner? _____

3. How many seventh graders spent less than $5 on dinner? _____

4. How many seventh graders spent $8–$10 on dinner? _____

5. What is the range of the price of dinner shown on the graph? _____

Extension Activity: Poll your classmates to find out their favorite television shows. You may want to just give them several to choose from. Then show your findings on a circle graph.

WAKE-UP WORD PROBLEM: Latasha polled 235 people about their favorite lunch meats. Sixty-seven percent of the people that Latasha polled said they liked turkey best. About how many of the people that Latasha polled liked turkey best?

Name: _____ Date: _____

Skill: Formulating questions that can be addressed with data and collecting, organizing, and displaying relevant data to answer them

Unit 5: Data Analysis and Probability: *Assessment 1*

Look at the circle graph. Then answer questions 1–2.

Average Amount of Time Spent on Homework

6th grade=1 hour, 30 minutes

7th grade=2 hours

8th grade=2 hours, 25 minutes

9th grade=3 hours

(based on poll of 325 students in Medina, California)

1. How many students were polled?
   - A. 350
   - B. 305
   - C. 225
   - D. 325

2. Based on the poll, what is the average amount of time students in all the grades have to study?
   - A. 2.23 hours
   - B. 2.25 hours
   - C. 2.23 minutes
   - D. 2.75 hours

Look at the Stem and Leaf Plot. Then answer questions 3–5.

Mary's History Grades

```
7 | 2  4  6  9
8 | 2  5  8  8
9 | 3  5  7  9
```

3. What is the median of all of Mary's history grades?
   - A. 86.5
   - B. 84.9
   - C. 82.7
   - D. 87.5

4. What is the mode of the data?
   - A. 76
   - B. 88
   - C. 74
   - D. 79

5. What was Mary's lowest grade?
   - A. 75
   - B. 72
   - C. 77
   - D. 81

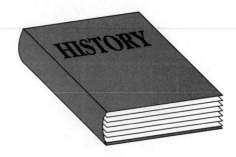

Name: _____ Date: _____

Unit 5: Data Analysis and Probability: *Assessment 1 (cont.)*

Look at the bar graph. Then answer questions 6–7.

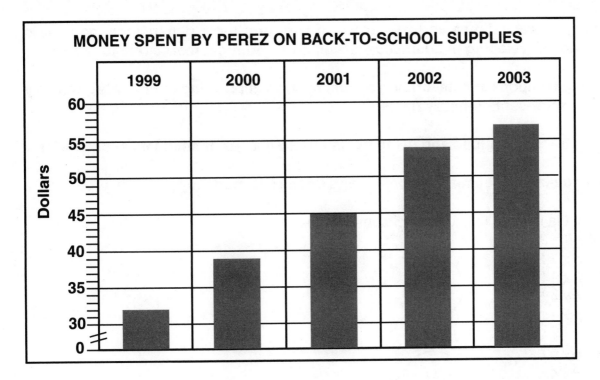

MONEY SPENT BY PEREZ ON BACK-TO-SCHOOL SUPPLIES

| 1999 | 2000 | 2001 | 2002 | 2003 |

6. How much money did Perez spend on school supplies in all five years?
   - ○ A. $241
   - ○ B. $227
   - ○ C. $239
   - ○ D. $217

7. How much more did Perez spend on school supplies in 2003 than in 2001?
   - ○ A. $14
   - ○ B. $8
   - ○ C. $15
   - ○ D. $12

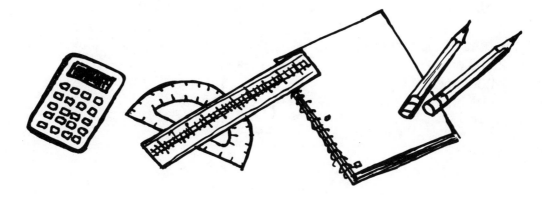

Name: _____ Date: _____

Review of Five Previously Taught NCTM Standards

- **Applying appropriate techniques, tools, and formulas to determine measurements**

- **Analyzing characteristics and properties of two- and three-dimensional geometric shapes, and developing mathematical arguments about geometric relationships**

- **Specifying locations and describing spatial relationships using coordinate geometry and other representational systems**

- **Applying transformations and using symmetry to analyze mathematical situations**

- **Using visualization, spatial reasoning, and geometric modeling to solve problems**

Mark the formula needed to find each circumference.

1. ○ A. $\pi \times 7.2$
    ○ B. $\pi \times 14.2$
    ○ C. $\pi \times 4.5$
    ○ D. $\pi \times 14.4$

r 7.2 cm

2. ○ A. $\pi \times 9.6$
    ○ B. $\pi \times 4.8$
    ○ C. $\pi \times 8.12$
    ○ D. $\pi \times 9.4$

r 4.8 in.

3. ○ A. $\pi \times 14.4$
    ○ B. $\pi \times 13.2$
    ○ C. $\pi \times 6.8$
    ○ D. $\pi \times 13.8$

r 6.9 mm

4. Find the volume of the rectangular prism.
    ○ A. 195.08 in.^{3}
    ○ B. 89.2 in.^{3}
    ○ C. 153.59 in.^{3}
    ○ D. 126.36 in.^{3}

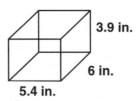

3.9 in.

6 in.

5.4 in.

5. Find the area of the rectangle.
    ○ A. 25.08 cm^2
    ○ B. 24.08 cm^2
    ○ C. 24.94 cm^2
    ○ D. 26.75 cm^2

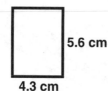

5.6 cm

4.3 cm

Name: _____ Date: _____

Review of Five Previously Taught NCTM Standards (cont.)

6. Simplify without using a calculator. $\sqrt{18}$
   - ○ A. ±4.98
   - ○ B. ±5.75
   - ○ C. ±4.64
   - ○ D. ±4.24

7. Which answer shows the point (-5,8) on the graph?

   ○ A.   ○ B.   ○ C.   ○ D.

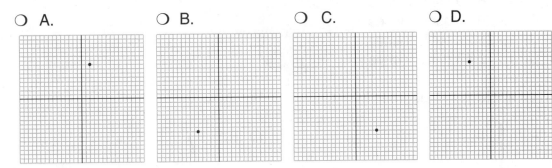

8. Which answer shows a rotation of the chair?

   ○ A.   ○ B.   ○ C.   ○ D.

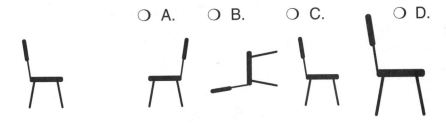

9. How many lines of symmetry does the clock have?
   - ○ A. 8
   - ○ B. 6
   - ○ C. 5
   - ○ D. 4

10. Which answer shows (-4,-1) on the graph?

   ○ A.   ○ B.   ○ C.   ○ D.

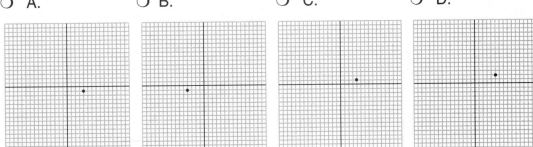

Name: _____ Date: _____

Review of Five Previously Taught NCTM Standards (cont.)

Find the volume of each sphere.

11. ○ A. 67.92 cubic feet
     ○ B. 65.45 cubic feet
     ○ C. 66.75 cubic feet
     ○ D. 68.25 cubic feet

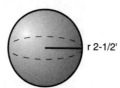

r 2-1/2'

12. ○ A. 1,476.89 cubic inches
     ○ B. 1,436.76 cubic inches
     ○ C. 1,475.29 cubic inches
     ○ D. 1,772.43 cubic inches

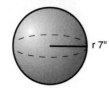

r 7"

13. Which angle is 171 degrees?

○ A.

○ B.

○ C.

○ D.

14. Which angle is 117 degrees?

○ A.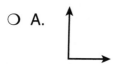

○ B.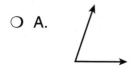

○ C.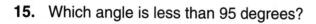

○ D.

15. Which angle is less than 95 degrees?

○ A.

○ B.

○ C.

○ D.

Name: _____ Date: _____

Skill: Selecting and using appropriate methods to analyze data

Unit 5: Data Analysis and Probability: *Practice Activity 7*

Just a Tip: The **mean** is the average. The **median** is the middle value of an ordered set or the average of the two middle values. The **mode** is the value occurring most often. The **range** is the difference between the highest and lowest values.

Find the mean, median, mode, and range of each set of data.

1. 78, 32, 34, 56, 78, 89, 95

    mean = _____   median = _____   mode = _____   range = _____

2. 12, 43, 67, 78, 99, 87, 67

    mean = _____   median = _____   mode = _____   range = _____

3. 90, 98, 87, 67, 56, 34, 32, 12, 44

    mean = _____   median = _____   mode = _____   range = _____

4. 123, 343, 543, 454, 434, 878, 989

    mean = _____   median = _____   mode = _____   range = _____

5. 343, 432, 878, 898, 909, 767, 787

    mean = _____   median = _____   mode = _____   range = _____

6. 676, 545, 343, 232, 122, 443, 700

    mean = _____   median = _____   mode = _____   range = _____

WAKE-UP WORD PROBLEM: Larry records his eight test grades in history class. His grades are 67, 75, 81, 89, 94, 97, 86, and 82. What is Larry's average score on all eight history tests?

_____

Name: _____ Date: _____

Skill: Selecting and using appropriate methods to analyze data

Unit 5: Data Analysis and Probability: *Assessment 2*

Find the mean for each set of data.

1. 1,232; 3,432; 4,534; 3,232; 2,323
   - ○ A. 2,980.8
   - ○ B. 2,950.6
   - ○ C. 2,110
   - ○ D. 3,220.5

2. 565, 343, 232, 878, 987, 900
   - ○ A. 650.83
   - ○ B. 605.87
   - ○ C. 650.89
   - ○ D. 666.82

Find the mode for each set of data.

3. 7,656; 3,432; 3,433; 5,454; 6,545
   - ○ A. 6,545
   - ○ B. 3,433
   - ○ C. 7,656
   - ○ D. all numbers occur equally

4. 987, 565, 767, 765, 565, 454, 323
   - ○ A. 565
   - ○ B. 767
   - ○ C. 765
   - ○ D. 323

Find the median for each set of data.

5. 2,011; 3,232; 7,765; 4,543; 4,343
   - ○ A. 4,343
   - ○ B. 3,232
   - ○ C. 2,011
   - ○ D. 4,543

6. 987, 454, 566, 343, 877, 999
   - ○ A. 566
   - ○ B. 721.5
   - ○ C. 877
   - ○ D. 999

Name: _____ Date: _____

Unit 5: Data Analysis and Probability: *Assessment 2 (cont.)*

Find the range for each set of data.

7. 1,786; 3,232; 3,432; 4,323; 5,434
- ○ A. 3,008
- ○ B. 2,778
- ○ C. 3,658
- ○ D. 3,648

8. 976, 343, 232, 865, 555, 841
- ○ A. 234
- ○ B. 744
- ○ C. 608
- ○ D. 754

Solve each problem.

9. Jacob records his first five grades in English class. They are 78, 79, 92, 85, and 79. Based on this information, what is Jacob's current average in English class?
- ○ A. 84.8
- ○ B. 87.9
- ○ C. 82.6
- ○ D. 68.7

10. Eight friends go shopping for prom dresses. They each find a prom dress they like. The costs of the dresses are as follows: $89, $99, $109, $121, $139, $141, $153, and $155. What is the average price of all eight prom dresses?
- ○ A. $117.78
- ○ B. $125.75
- ○ C. $186.95
- ○ D. $165.55

Name: _____ Date: _____

Skill: Understanding and applying basic concepts of probability

Unit 5: Data Analysis and Probability: *Practice Activity 8*

Just a Tip: Probability tells you how likely something is to happen. The probability for equally likely outcomes is $P = E/N$, where E equals the number of possible outcomes in which the event occurs, and N equals the number of equally likely/possible outcomes.

Complete the table describing the probability.

In words	As a fraction	As a decimal	As a percent
1. 1 in 4 chance	_____	_____	_____
2. 5 chances out of 8	_____	_____	_____
3. 50–50 chance	_____	_____	_____
4. 90–10 chance	_____	_____	_____
5. 1 in 3 chance	_____	_____	_____
6. impossible	_____	_____	_____
7. 70–30 chance	_____	_____	_____
8. 40–60 chance	_____	_____	_____
9. 3 in 4 chance	_____	_____	_____
10. certain	_____	_____	_____

Name: _____ Date: _____

Skill: Understanding and applying basic concepts of probability

Unit 5: Data Analysis and Probability: *Practice Activity 9*

Look at the spinner. Then answer the five questions.

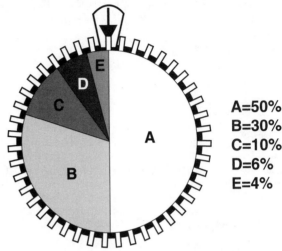

1. What percentage represents the chance the spinner will land on C? _____

2. What percentage represents the chance the spinner will land on A or C? _____

3. Which decimal represents the chance the spinner will land on D? _____

4. Which fraction represents the chance the spinner will land on D or E? _____

5. Which fraction represents the chance the spinner will land on A or E? _____

A=50%
B=30%
C=10%
D=6%
E=4%

The probabilities of two events are given. Tell which event is more likely to happen.

6. The probability of event A is $\frac{3}{9}$. _____
   The probability of event B is $\frac{5}{8}$.

7. The probability of event A is $\frac{1}{4}$. _____
   The probability of event B is $\frac{7}{12}$.

8. The probability of event A is $\frac{2}{3}$. _____
   The probability of event B is $\frac{1}{2}$.

9. The probability of event A is $\frac{6}{9}$. _____
   The probability of event B is $\frac{2}{7}$.

10. The probability of event A is $\frac{1}{2}$. _____
    The probability of event B is $\frac{3}{4}$.

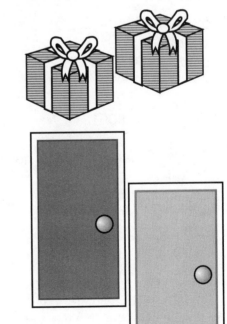

Name: _____ Date: _____

Skill: Understanding and applying basic concepts of probability

Unit 5: Data Analysis and Probability: *Assessment 3*

1. Mark has a 1 in 6 chance of winning the race. What fraction represents the probability that Mark will win the race?
   - ○ A. $\frac{1}{4}$
   - ○ B. $\frac{1}{6}$
   - ○ C. $\frac{1}{2}$
   - ○ D. $\frac{2}{3}$

2. What decimal represents an 80–20 chance?
   - ○ A. 8.78
   - ○ B. 0.5
   - ○ C. 0.72
   - ○ D. 0.8

3. What percentage represents a 90–10 chance?
   - ○ A. 90%
   - ○ B. 87%
   - ○ C. 85%
   - ○ D. 91%

4. What decimal represents a 2 in 10 chance?
   - ○ A. 0.38
   - ○ B. 0.2
   - ○ C. 2.08
   - ○ D. 0.58

Marty, Sam, and Paige enter a raffle to win a chance to be principal for the day. Three hundred and fifty other students enter the raffle as well. All of the other students, besides the ones listed, bought only one ticket each. Marty buys 4 tickets, Sam buys 6 tickets, and Paige buys 9 tickets. Based on this information, answer questions 5–8.

5. Marty has a ___ chance of winning the raffle.
   - ○ A. 0.01084
   - ○ B. 1.09878
   - ○ C. 0.026781
   - ○ D. 0.00012

6. Sam has a ___ chance of winning the raffle.
   - ○ A. 0.01654
   - ○ B. 0.01626
   - ○ C. 0.66756
   - ○ D. 0.00921

7. Paige has a ___ chance of winning the raffle.
   - ○ A. 0.43892
   - ○ B. 0.00439
   - ○ C. 0.02439
   - ○ D. 0.32121

RAFFLE

012857

8. The probability of event A is $\frac{2}{7}$. The probability of event B is $\frac{5}{9}$. Based on this information, which of the following statements is true?
   - ○ A. Event A is more likely.
   - ○ B. Event B is more likely.
   - ○ C. Events A and B are equally likely.
   - ○ D. Events A and B are not likely.

Name: _____ Date: _____

End-of-Book Review

1. Name the place of the number in bold: 7**8**6,425,304
   - ○ A. 80 million
   - ○ B. 80 thousand
   - ○ C. 80 hundred
   - ○ D. 80 billion

2. Which choice shows the number written in standard form?
   Sixteen million, four hundred thousand, six hundred eighty-four
   - ○ A. 16,497,987
   - ○ B. 16,440,684
   - ○ C. 16,564,987
   - ○ D. 16,400,684

3. Rewrite the number in scientific notation: 800
   - ○ A. 8×10^4
   - ○ B. 8×10^2
   - ○ C. 8×10^1
   - ○ D. 8×10^5

4. Which decimal is equal to the fraction $\frac{7}{12}$?
   - ○ A. 0.585
   - ○ B. 0.583
   - ○ C. 0.787
   - ○ D. 0.908

5. Evaluate the algebraic expression if $b = 3$, $c = 4$, and $d = 5$.
   $2d \div b =$
   - ○ A. 3.38
   - ○ B. 3.35
   - ○ C. 3.33
   - ○ D. 333

6. Use the order of operations to evaluate the expression.
   $12(18 - 5) + 64 =$
   - ○ A. 122
   - ○ B. 214
   - ○ C. 224
   - ○ D. 220

7. Simplify the radical without using a calculator. $\sqrt{9}$
   - ○ A. ±4
   - ○ B. ±3
   - ○ C. ±2
   - ○ D. ±12

Name: _____ Date: _____

End-of-Book Review (cont.)

8. Solve. 7.86 + 0.889 =
   - ○ A. 8.889
   - ○ B. 8.749
   - ○ C. 9.992
   - ○ D. 8.078

9. Analyze the algorithm 4,186 ÷ 12 =
   - ○ A. 0.348
   - ○ B. 3.48
   - ○ C. 3,048
   - ○ D. 348.8

10. Solve the proportion. $\dfrac{10}{40} = \dfrac{b}{60}$
    - ○ A. $b = 25$
    - ○ B. $b = 12$
    - ○ C. $b = 10$
    - ○ D. $b = 15$

11. Solve. Eighteen more than a number, divided by 3
    - ○ A. $x - 18 \div 3$
    - ○ B. $x + (18 \div 3)$
    - ○ C. $x \div 3 - 18$
    - ○ D. $(x + 18) \div 3$

12. Solve. 6×10^3
    - ○ A. 600
    - ○ B. 6,000
    - ○ C. 600,000
    - ○ D. 6,000,000

13. Find the area of the square.
    - ○ A. 40 sq. cm
    - ○ B. 35 sq. cm
    - ○ C. 28 sq. cm
    - ○ D. 25 sq. cm

    5 cm

14. Find the surface area of a cylinder with base diameter = 1.4, height = 2.2 inches.
    - ○ A. 12.76 inches squared
    - ○ B. 127.6 inches squared
    - ○ C. 117.8 inches squared
    - ○ D. 1276.9 inches squared

15. Find the volume of a sphere with radius = 6 centimeters.
    - ○ A. 908.76 cm^3
    - ○ B. 904.78 cm^3
    - ○ C. 917.56 cm^3
    - ○ D. 928.95 cm^3

16. Molly's math grades are 76, 79, 82, 87, and 94. What is the mean of all of Molly's math grades?
    - ○ A. 86%
    - ○ B. 84%
    - ○ C. 82%
    - ○ D. 85%

17. Which formula is needed to find the circumference of a circle?
    - ○ A. πd
    - ○ B. πr
    - ○ C. $\pi \times 9$
    - ○ D. $\pi \times 8.45$

18. Which angle is 118 degrees?
    - ○ A.
    - ○ B.
    - ○ C.
    - ○ D.

Name: _____   Date: _____

End-of-Book Review (cont.)

Use the coordinate grid to answer questions 19–20.

19. Which coordinate pair is the location of point G?
- ○ A. (-2,4)
- ○ B. (6,3)
- ○ C. (3,-4)
- ○ D. (4,-2)

20. Which point is located at (2,6)?
- ○ A. C
- ○ B. H
- ○ C. J
- ○ D. B

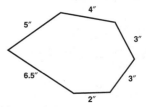

21. Find the volume of the rectangular prism.
- ○ A. 1,550.4 cm³
- ○ B. 100.6 cm³
- ○ C. 228 cm²
- ○ D. 1,248.9 cm²

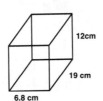

22. Find the area of the triangle.
- ○ A. 112 in.²
- ○ B. 98 in.²
- ○ C. 56 in.²
- ○ D. 22 in.²

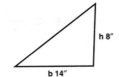

23. Find the perimeter of the pentagon.
s = 6.2 cm
- ○ A. 11.2 cm
- ○ B. 31 cm
- ○ C. 38.4 cm
- ○ D. 36 cm

24. Find the perimeter of the irregular shape.
- ○ A. 23.5 in.
- ○ B. 22.5 in.
- ○ C. 26 in.
- ○ D. 48 in.

25. Which unit of measurement would be the best for measuring the weight of bags of Halloween treats?
- ○ A. quarts
- ○ B. tons
- ○ C. centimeters
- ○ D. ounces

Answer Keys

Unit 1: Practice Activity 1 (p. 2)
1. hundred thousands
2. ten millions
3. ten thousands
4. ten millions
5. hundredths
6. tenths
7. hundreds
8. hundredths
9. thousandths
10. tenths
11. four million, seven hundred eighty-six thousand, nine hundred twenty-one
12. thirty-three million, seven hundred eighty-one thousand, four hundred forty-one
13. two million, four hundred sixty-eight thousand, two hundred ninety-one
14. seventeen million, two hundred sixty-four thousand, five hundred twenty-one
15. four hundred fifty-two and ninety-seven thousandths
16. 700,000,000
17. 16,488
18. 75,004
19. 65,000,058
20. 173.13

Wake-Up Word Problem: Peggy saved $568.

Unit 1: Practice Activity 2 (p. 3)
1. 0.041, 0.066, 0.092, 7.62
2. 0.034, 0.043, 0.826, 7.28
3. 0.045, 0.27, 0.789, 2.7
4. 0.321, 3.21, 4.05, 32.1
5. 0.29, 0.65, 0.75, 0.78
6. 15.7, 1.5, 0.012, 0.011
7. 0.61, 0.077, 0.072, 0.068
8. 5.75, 0.65, 0.56, 0.290
9. 30.7, 2.35, 0.405, 0.395
10. 4.11, 0.288, 0.276, 0.028
11. $\frac{1}{3}, \frac{1}{2}, \frac{5}{8}, \frac{3}{4}$
12. $\frac{1}{4}, \frac{1}{3}, \frac{5}{11}, \frac{7}{9}$
13. $\frac{3}{4}, \frac{5}{7}, \frac{3}{5}, \frac{1}{2}$

14. $\frac{2}{3}, \frac{5}{9}, \frac{1}{3}$
15. $\frac{7}{8}, \frac{5}{12}, \frac{1}{3}, \frac{1}{4}$

Unit 1: Practice Activity 3 (p. 4)
1. 36
2. 4,096
3. 128
4. 5
5. 1
6. 100
7. 1,000
8. 10,000
9. 100,000
10. 1,000,000
11. 9×10^2
12. 5×10^5
13. 2.704×10^6
14. 6.581×10^1
15. 4×10^8
16. 7.841×10^{10}
17. 7.687×10^2
18. 8×10^7
19. 3×10^3
20. 6.8427×10^9

Unit 1: Practice Activity 4 (p. 5)
1. 0.9
2. 0.17
3. 0.8
4. 0.63
5. 1.4
6. 0.072
7. 0.6
8. 0.875
9. 0.5
10. 0.75
11. 0.667
12. 0.667
13. 0.25
14. 0.833
15. 0.375

86

Unit 1: Assessment 1 (p. 6–7)

1. D
2. A
3. C
4. B
5. C
6. C
7. B
8. D
9. B
10. B
11. B
12. A
13. D
14. D
15. C

Unit 1: Practice Activity 5 (p. 8)

1. 64
2. 10
3. 3
4. -22
5. 28
6. 9
7. 59
8. 74
9. 116
10. 39
11. 291
12. 10
13. 21
14. 225
15. 4

Unit 1: Practice Activity 6 (p. 9)

1. 57
2. 9,604
3. 55
4. 16
5. 18
6. 65
7. 216
8. 49
9. 18
10. -70
11. 196
12. 554
13. 99
14. 256
15. 18

Unit 1: Practice Activity 7 (p. 10)

1. 74
2. 246
3. 52
4. 138
5. 167
6. 74
7. 228
8. 1,114
9. 622
10. 1,137
11. 44
12. 158

Wake-Up Word Problem: Charlene saved $17.85 during the entire six weeks.

Unit 1: Practice Activity 8 (p. 11)

1. ±5
2. ±4
3. ±2
4. ±6
5. ±10
6. ±11
7. ±3
8. ±9
9. ±7
10. ±8
11. ±3.464
12. ±4.899
13. ±4.243
14. ±0.707
15. ±1.414

Unit 1: Assessment 2 (p. 12)

1. A
2. B
3. C
4. D
5. D
6. C
7. A
8. A
9. B
10. C

Unit 1: Practice Activity 9 (p. 13)
1. 0.443
2. 0.055
3. 12.19
4. 5.34
5. 0.125
6. 1.769
7. $\frac{7}{8}$
8. $\frac{17}{18}$
9. $\frac{13}{8}$ or $1\frac{5}{8}$
10. $\frac{3}{4}$
11. $2\frac{2}{9}$
12. $6\frac{3}{4}$
13. 165.44
14. 353.76
15. 3.78
16. 435.8
17. 3.6
18. 485.94
19. 492.6
20. 113.58
21. 1,364.42
22. 366.85
23. 9.633
24. 240.33
25. 9,053.75

Unit 1: Practice Activity 10 (p. 14)
1. 0.483
2. 0.625
3. 157.96
4. 199
5. $2\frac{21}{32}$
6. $34\frac{5}{6}$
7. 0.09858
8. 4.2822
9. $2\frac{1}{4}$
10. 318.75

Wake-Up Word Problem: Theresa will put 87 marbles in each pile, with 2 marbles left over.

11. $x = 28$
12. $b = 3$
13. $x = 136$
14. $y = 90$

15. $y = 72$
16. $x = 42$
17. $y = 9$
18. $y = 4.8$
19. $x = 72$
20. $y = 3.86$

Unit 1: Assessment 3 (p. 15)
1. B
2. D
3. D
4. B
5. B
6. B
7. A
8. B
9. C
10. D

Review of Three Previously Taught NCTM Standards (p. 16–17)
1. B
2. D
3. D
4. A
5. C
6. A
7. B
8. B
9. B
10. C

Unit 2: Practice Activity 1 (p. 18)
1. $x \cdot y = y \cdot x$
2. $x \cdot x \cdot x = x^3$
3. 75% of $x = \frac{3}{4} \cdot x$
4. 25% of $x = \frac{1}{4}$ of x

Unit 2: Practice Activity 2 (p. 19)
1. Each insect has six legs; # insects (I) x 6
2. Each octopus has eight arms; # octopuses (O) x 8
3. Each dime has a value of $0.10; # of dimes (D) x $0.10

Unit 2: Practice Activity 3 (p. 20)

1. Equation: $e = \$18 + 3(w - 1)$. Since the graph forms a straight line, it tells you that Kelly is making a constant amount of money.

Kelly's Earnings

Wake-Up Word Problem: Louise has $263.40 in her account now.

Unit 2: Practice Activity 4 (p. 21)

2. Student answers should be graphed.
3. Student answers should be graphed.
4. Student answers should be graphed.

Unit 2: Assessment 1 (p. 22–23)

1. A
2. C
3. D
4. D
5. C
6. A
7. D

Unit 2: Practice Activity 5 (p. 24)

1. $10 - 4$
2. $6 \cdot 7$
3. $\frac{1}{2}n + 5$
4. $(x + 6)/2$
5. $x^2 - 5$
6. $19 - 7$
7. $7 \cdot 2$
8. $4 - 7$
9. $x^2 - 8$

10. $8n + 5$
11. $6n + 4 \cdot 3$
12. $64 \div 4$
13. $10 + 8n$
14. $n/7$
15. $11 - 4n$

Unit 2: Practice Activity 6 (p. 25)

Teacher check graphs.

Unit 2: Assessment 2 (p. 26–27)

1. A
2. B
3. D
4. A
5. C
6. B
7. A
8. B
9. B
10. A

Unit 2: Practice Activity 7 (p. 28)

1. 200
2. 300,000,000
3. 5,000,000
4. 40,000
5. 12,000
6. 1,500
7. 390,625
8. 20
9. $1\frac{1}{14}$
10. $\frac{1}{6}$
11. $\frac{3}{16}$
12. $\frac{10}{21}$
13. -32
14. 18
15. -55

Wake-Up Word Problem: José's average deposit was $90.89.

Unit 2: Practice Activity 8 (p. 29)
1. 9.75
2. quotient 9, remainder 6
3. 75
4. the reciprocal of *b* or $\frac{1}{b}$
5. $x \cdot 1/y$
6. $2\frac{1}{4}$
7. $1\frac{6}{19}$

Unit 2: Practice Activity 9 (p. 30)
1. 49.06
2. 14.58
3. 28.36
4. 83 feet, 4 inches
5. 205.67
6. Jeremy will put two in each box. He will have eighteen left over.
7. 276
8. 52 teams, 5 players are left over

Unit 2: Assessment 3 (p. 31)
1. A
2. B
3. C
4. C
5. A
6. A
7. B
8. A
9. A
10. B

Unit 3: Practice Activity 1 (p. 32)
Students should have followed directions given. Teacher check.

Unit 3: Practice Activity 2 (p. 33)
1. 31,680
2. 27
3. 144
4. 15
5. 112
6. 5
7. 5
8. 8

9. 20
10. 1.89
11. 38.10
12. 3.11

Unit 3: Practice Activity 3 (p. 34)
1. 10 degrees
2. 95 degrees
3. 115 degrees
4. 55 degrees
5. 85 degrees
6. 160 degrees
7. 50 degrees
8. A
9. A
10. B

Unit 3: Practice Activity 4 (p. 35)
1. 4 cm^2
2. 225 ft.^2
3. 144 ft.^2
4. 16 cm^2
5. 36 cm^2
6. 512 cm^3
7. 216 mm^3
8. 64 yds.^3
9. 125 ft.^3
10. $1,000 \text{ in.}^3$

Wake-Up Word Problem: The area of the square is 5,625 square feet.

Unit 3: Assessment 1 (p. 36–37)
1. A
2. D
3. B
4. B
5. A
6. B
7. B
8. A
9. D
10. B

Review of Four Previously Taught NCTM Standards (p. 38–39)

1. A
2. B
3. D
4. A
5. D
6. A
7. C
8. B
9. B
10. D

Unit 3: Practice Activity 5 (p. 40)

1. $\pi(4.2)$; $3.1416 \times 4.2 = 13.19472$ cm
2. $\pi(6 \times 2)$; $3.1416 \times 12 = 37.6992$ cm
3. $\pi(5 \times 2)$; $3.1416 \times 10 = 31.416$ cm
4. $\pi(3.4)$; $3.1416 \times 3.4 = 10.68144$ mm
5. $\pi(4.1 \times 2)$; $3.1416 \times 8.2 = 25.76112$ mm
6. 28.9 cm
7. 8.8 mm
8. 44.0 ft.
9. 25.1 ft.
10. 16.0 in.

Unit 3: Practice Activity 6 (p. 41)

1. 17.53 inches^2
2. 36.52 centimeters^2
3. 65.42 centimeters^2
4. 149.23 centimeters^2
5. 547.96 centimeters^2

Unit 3: Practice Activity 7 (p. 42)

1. 378 in.^{3}
2. $2{,}309.076$ cm^3
3. 240 cm^3
4. 763.41 in.^{3}
5. $1{,}680$ cm^3

Unit 3: Practice Activity 8 (p. 43)

1. 20.28 cm^2
2. 22.6875 in.^{2}
3. 378 ft.^{2}
4. 94.5 cm^2
5. 19 cm^2
6. 29.7 in.^{2}
7. 40 ft.^{2}
8. 90 in.^{2}
9. 17.6 cm
10. 11.518 in.

Unit 3: Assessment 2 (p. 44–45)

1. A
2. B
3. C
4. D
5. B
6. A
7. D
8. C
9. B
10. B

Unit 4: Practice Activity 1 (p. 46)

1. ± 7
2. ± 7.48
3. ± 8
4. ± 9.54
5. ± 6
6. ± 6.93
7. ± 5.20
8. ± 11.18
9. ± 3
10. ± 5.29

Wake-Up Word Problem: The three friends spent an average of $16.23.

Unit 4: Practice Activity 2 (p. 47)

Answers will vary. Teacher check.

Unit 4: Practice Activity 3 (p. 48)

1. $c = 35.78$
2. $a = 43.82$
3. $c = 79.06$
4. $a = 47.92$
5. $a = 42.41$

Unit 4: Assessment 1 (p. 49–50)

1. B
2. A
3. A
4. C
5. A
6. B
7. A
8. B
9. C
10. D

Unit 4: Practice Activity 4 (p. 51)

Students should have graphed the points on the graph.

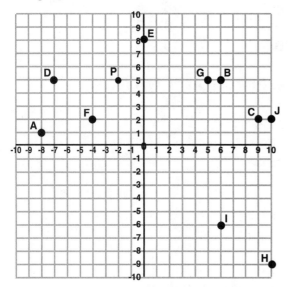

Unit 4: Practice Activity 5 (p. 52)

1.	(-4,2)	**2.**	(-6,8)
3.	(9,3)	**4.**	(7,2)
5.	(8,4)	**6.**	(-3,-5)
7.	(9,1)	**8.**	(11,3)
9.	(12,1)	**10.**	(-7,3)

Unit 4: Practice Activity 6 (p. 53)

Students should have graphed the points given.

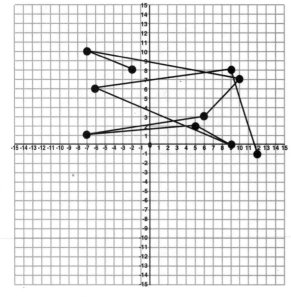

Wake-Up Word Problem: Tonya puts $293.25 in each account.

Unit 4: Assessment 2 (p. 54–55)

1.	A	**2.**	B
3.	D	**4.**	C
5.	A	**6.**	D
7.	B	**8.**	C
9.	D	**10.**	A

Unit 4: Practice Activity 7 (p. 56)

1. A
2. A
3. C
4. B

Unit 4: Practice Activity 8 (p. 57)

Students should have drawn reflections.

Unit 4: Practice Activity 9 (p. 58)

Students should have drawn in lines of symmetry.

Unit 4: Practice Activity 10 (p. 59)

Students' work should show congruent figures.

Wake-Up Word Problem: About 38,658 of the people at the game are over eighteen years old.

Unit 4: Assessment 3 (p. 60–61)

1.	B	**2.**	A
3.	D	**4.**	B
5.	A	**6.**	B
7.	A	**8.**	B
9.	D	**10.**	A

Unit 4: Practice Activity 11 (p. 62)

1. 2144.67 cubic centimeters
2. 179.59 cubic inches
3. 523.60 cubic inches
4. 3,053.64 cubic centimeters
5. 65.45 cubic inches
6. 1,320 cubic millimeters
7. 142.5 cubic inches
8. 864 cubic inches
9. 146.25 cubic centimeters
10. 504 cubic inches

Unit 4: Practice Activity 12 (p. 63)

1–5. Students should have drawn in all described shapes.

Students should have drawn in the following:

6. 87-degree angle
7. 99-degree angle
8. 108-degree angle
9. 178-degree angle
10. 121-degree angle

Wake-Up Word Problem: Henry spent $870.

Unit 4: Assessment 4 (p. 64–65)

1. A		**2.** C	
3. D		**4.** A	
5. B		**6.** B	
7. A		**8.** C	
9. B		**10.** A	

Unit 5: Practice Activity 1 (p. 66)

1. about 95 students
2. 112 students
3. about 116 students
4. about 25 students
5. (350)(0.27) + (350)(0.33) + (350)(0.07) + (350)(.01) = x or 350 - 350 (0.32) = x

Unit 5: Practice Activity 2 (p. 67)

1. 125
2. 90
3. 305
4. 195
5. 500
6. $\frac{21}{100}$
7. $\frac{1}{4}$
8. 105

Unit 5: Practice Activity 3 (p. 68)

1. 8
2. 26
3. all numbers occur equally
4. 82%
5. Answers will vary.

Unit 5: Practice Activity 4 (p. 69)

1. $2,000
2. $31,157.50
3. $28,417
4. $29,125
5. Answers will vary. Example: Median income tends to rise.
6. Students should have created bar graphs based on the information provided.

Unit 5: Practice Activity 5 (p. 70)

1. 128
2. 111
3. 84
4. 27
5. 195

Unit 5: Practice Activity 6 (p. 71)

1. About 32
2. About 23
3. 51
4. 45
5. $0–infinity

Wake-Up Word Problem: About 157 people liked turkey best.

Unit 5: Assessment 1 (p. 72–73)

1. D
2. A
3. A
4. B
5. B
6. B
7. D

Review of Five Previously Taught NCTM Standards (p. 74–76)

1. D		**2.** A	
3. D		**4.** D	
5. B		**6.** D	
7. D		**8.** B	
9. A		**10.** B	
11. B		**12.** B	
13. D		**14.** D	
15. B			

Unit 5: Practice Activity 7 (p. 77)

1. 66, 78, 78, 63
2. 64.71, 67, 67, 87
3. 57.78, 56, all numbers occur equally, 86
4. 537.71, 454, all numbers occur equally, 866
5. 716.29, 787, all numbers occur equally, 566
6. 437.29, 443, all numbers occur equally, 578

Wake-Up Word Problem: Larry's average score is 84%.

Unit 5: Assessment 2 (p. 78–79)

1. B	2. A
3. D	4. A
5. A	6. B
7. D	8. B
9. C	10. B

Unit 5: Practice Activity 8 (p. 80)

1. $\frac{1}{4}$, 0.25, 25%
2. $\frac{5}{8}$, 0.625, 62.5%
3. $\frac{1}{2}$, 0.5, 50%
4. $\frac{9}{10}$, 0.9, 90%
5. $\frac{1}{3}$, 0.33, 33%
6. 0, 0.0, 0%
7. $\frac{7}{10}$, 0.7, 70%
8. $\frac{2}{5}$, 0.40, 40%
9. $\frac{3}{4}$, 0.75, 75%
10. 1, 1, 100%

Unit 5: Practice Activity 9 (p. 81)

1. 10%
2. 60%
3. 0.06
4. $\frac{1}{10}$
5. $\frac{27}{50}$

The event that is more probable is:

6. B
7. B
8. A
9. A
10. B

Unit 5: Assessment 3 (p. 82)

1. B
2. D
3. A
4. B
5. A
6. B
7. C
8. B

End-of-Book Review (p. 83–85)

1. A		2. D
3. B		4. B
5. C		6. D
7. B		8. B
9. D		10. D
11. D		12. B
13. D		14. A
15. B		16. B
17. A		18. B
19. A		20. D
21. A		22. C
23. B		24. A
25. D		